Sacred Music

Part 1

Recent Researches in Music

A-R Editions publishes seven series of critical editions, spanning the history of Western music, American music, and oral traditions.

Recent Researches in the Music of the Middle Ages and Early Renaissance
    Charles M. Atkinson, general editor

Recent Researches in the Music of the Renaissance
    James Haar, general editor

Recent Researches in the Music of the Baroque Era
    Christoph Wolff, general editor

Recent Researches in the Music of the Classical Era
    Neal Zaslaw, general editor

Recent Researches in the Music of the Nineteenth and Early Twentieth Centuries
    Rufus Hallmark, general editor

Recent Researches in American Music
    John M. Graziano, general editor

Recent Researches in the Oral Traditions of Music
    Philip V. Bohlman, general editor

Each edition in *Recent Researches* is devoted to works by a single composer or to a single genre. The content is chosen for its high quality and historical importance and is edited according to the scholarly standards that govern the making of all reliable editions.

For information on establishing a standing order to any of our series, or for editorial guidelines on submitting proposals, please contact:

A-R Editions, Inc.
Middleton, Wisconsin

800 736-0070 (North American book orders)
608 836-9000 (phone)
608 831-8200 (fax)
http://www.areditions.com

RECENT RESEARCHES IN THE MUSIC OF THE BAROQUE ERA, 164

Antoine Boesset

Sacred Music

Part 1
Motets and Hymns

Edited by Peter Bennett

A-R Editions, Inc.
Middleton, Wisconsin

A-R Editions, Inc., Middleton, Wisconsin
© 2010 by A-R Editions, Inc.

All rights reserved. No part of this book may be reproduced or transmitted in any form by any electronic or mechanical means (including photocopying, recording, or information storage and retrieval) without permission in writing from the publisher.

The purchase of this edition does not convey the right to perform it in public, nor to make a recording of it for any purpose. Such permission must be obtained in advance from the publisher.

A-R Editions is pleased to support scholars and performers in their use of *Recent Researches* material for study or performance. Subscribers to any of the *Recent Researches* series, as well as patrons of subscribing institutions, are invited to apply for information about our "Copyright Sharing Policy."

Printed in the United States of America

ISBN-13: 978-0-89579-676-9
ISBN-10: 0-89579-676-7
ISSN: 0484-0828

♾ The paper used in this publication meets the minimum requirements of the American National Standard for Information Sciences—Permanence of Paper for Printed Library Materials, ANSI Z39.48-1992.

Contents

Acknowledgments vii

Introduction ix
   The Royal Abbey of Montmartre ix
   The Composer x
   "Boesset" Attributions in Rés. 571 xi
   The Music of the Edition xiv
   Notes on Performance xv
   Notes xvii

Texts and Translations xix

Plates xxxii

Motets
   1. Alma Redemptoris Mater 3
   2. Anna mater Matris 7
   3. Ave Maria (1) 13
   4. Ave Maria (2) 20
   5. Ave per cor suavissimum Jesu 24
   6. Ave Regina caelorum 28
   7. Ave salus mundi 32
   8. Ave virginum gemma Catharina 36
   9. Benedicimus te 39
   10. Domine salvum fac regem (1) 44
   11. Domine salvum fac regem (2) 48
   12. Domine salvum fac regem (3) 50
   13. Domine salvum fac regem (4) 57
   14. Duo seraphim 59
       14a. Duo seraphim (alternative opening) 63
   15. Ecce panis Angelorum 64
   16. Fons aquae vivae 66
   17. Hic est beatissimus 72
   18. O athletum invictissimum 76
   19. O crux ave 82
   20. O Doctor optime 84
   21. O Pastor aeterne 90
   22. O quam suavis 93
   23. O sacrum convivium 96
   24. Popule meus 98
   25. Pretiosus Domini Dionysius 102
   26. Regina caeli (1) 106

27. Regina caeli (2) 111
28. Regina caeli (3) 114
29. Regnum mundi 117
30. Salve Regina (1) 121
31. Salve Regina (2) 126
32. Salve Regina (3) 131
33. Sancta Maria 136
34. Tu es Petrus 139
35. Tu es vas electionis 143
36. Veni Sancte Spiritus 150
37. Vir Domini Benedictus 153

Hymns

38. Ad caenam Agni *(alternatim)* 158
39. Alleluja. O filii et filiae 159
40. Aurea luce *(alternatim)* 167
41. Ave maris stella *(alternatim)* 171
42. Ave mater pia *(alternatim)* 175
43. Christe redemptor omnium, Conserva *(alternatim)* 178
44. Christe redemptor omnium, Ex Patre 181
45. Claris conjubila *(alternatim)* 182
46. Dionysii martyris *(alternatim)* 186
47. Iste Confessor *(alternatim)* 190
48. Jesu, nostra redemptio *(alternatim)* 193
49. O gloriosae virgines 197
50. O salutaris hostia 199
51. Pange lingua . . . Corporis 201
52. Pange lingua . . . Certaminis 205
53. Quam pulchra es 208
　　53a. Quam pulchra es (alternative refrain) 210
54. Veni Creator Spiritus *(alternatim)* 211

Critical Report 217

Sources 217
Editorial Methods 217
Critical Commentary 218

Appendix

Pange lingua . . . Certaminis, verse 2 223

Acknowledgments

Work on this edition was greatly assisted by a number of individuals and organizations. I am grateful to Catherine Massip and the staff at the Music Department of the Bibliothèque nationale de France for their assistance and courtesy and for permission to publish photographic reproductions. I am also indebted to my godparents, Jean and Bernard Lefèvre, whose hospitality in Paris enabled me to carry out the research that led to this edition. A W. P. Jones Faculty Development grant from Case Western Reserve University enabled me to complete my work in a timely manner, as did the assistance of Nathaniel Wood, who helped with preliminary stages of the edition. Finally, I am grateful to Jean Duron and Thomas Lecomte of the Centre de Musique Baroque à Versailles for their stimulating comments about Boesset and sacred music, and for the support of numerous other colleagues who share my interest in bringing the music of Louis XIII to a wider audience.

Introduction

The study of Latin sacred music composed in France during the reign of Louis XIII (1610–43) has long been hampered by the scarcity of surviving musical sources from the period. In part due to the unusual circumstances in which music publishing developed in France,[1] and possibly in part due to the destruction of church property during the Revolution nearly two centuries later, only a handful of printed and manuscript sources testify to the musical activity in the churches and chapels of Paris during the first half of the seventeenth century. As a result of this paucity, historians have generally characterized the reign of Louis XIII as a period in which little music of any value was composed, and in which composers slavishly continued the practices of the sixteenth century or composed music little more sophisticated than fauxbourdon. Certainly, apart from clearly retrospective publications such as Eustache du Caurroy's *Preces ecclesiasticae* (1609), the very few other sources from the period, such as Jean de Bournonville's *Octo cantica* (1612/25), Charles d'Ambleville's two collections of *Harmonia sacra* (1636), and Nicolas Formé's two volumes of *Musica simplex* (1638) preserve a strictly functional, often fauxbourdon-inspired repertory intended for practical use among moderately proficient provincial or parish choirs—although Formé's collection may also have been used at the Chapelle Royale, where he was *sous-maître* until 1638.[2] Works of higher status, such as the masses composed for Notre Dame by Henri Frémart[3] and Formé's set of Magnificats in the eight church tones,[4] are somewhat more sophisticated, but nevertheless employ a musical language firmly rooted in the imitative polyphony of the sixteenth century.

By contrast, apart from Formé's two surviving motets and the mass *Aeternae Henrici magni* for double choir (published in 1638 and thus originating toward the end of the period under consideration),[5] the only works generally considered to show any more forward-looking features are those now attributed to Guillaume Bouzignac. Preserved in two anonymous manuscript sources, some of Bouzignac's surviving works clearly exhibit a madrigalian and dramatic style possibly resulting from Italian and Spanish influences in the south of France (where Bouzignac was active), but this music neither makes use of the basse continue nor shows any influence of contemporary Italian monody. Thus, in light of the available published and manuscript sources, scholars have generally agreed that sacred music in France only began to be "modernized" with the arrival of Henri Dumont in the country around 1640, the introduction of the basse continue in his *Cantica sacra* (1652), and the creation of the *grand motet* in the early 1660s.[6]

The works presented in this edition paint a different picture. A reassessment of the so-called Deslauriers manuscript reveals that this music, all of it previously believed to date from the reign of Louis XIV and some of it attributed to Jean-Baptiste Boesset (1614–85), in fact emerged several decades earlier and was composed by Jean-Baptiste's father Antoine (1586–1643), the most prominent composer of the day and *surintendant de la musique de la chambre* in Louis XIII's court.[7] Composed primarily for the nuns of the Royal Abbey of Montmartre and consisting of over seventy liturgical works scored for multiple high voices, bass voice, and basse continue, this newly identified body of music represents by far the largest repertory of sacred music from the reign of Louis XIII. While not showing the influence of the newest Italian practices, this music nevertheless anticipates several of the musical techniques previously associated with Dumont's 1652 publication, in particular the use of the basse continue. Antoine Boesset's music for Montmartre thus fills a significant gap in our understanding of musical developments in seventeenth-century France and demonstrates that sacred music of the highest quality emerged during a period that scholars have long dismissed as being of little interest.

The Royal Abbey of Montmartre

The Royal Abbey of Montmartre was one of the most symbolically important religious houses in France until its destruction during the French Revolution. In Roman times, the hill just outside Paris on which the abbey was later located was home to a number of temples to Mercury and Mars, but by the eighth century a church with a wooden nave, dedicated to Saint Denis, had been built there.[8] According to Abbott Hilduin (writing in the year 836), the church commemorated the martyrdom of Saint Denis, who, together with his companions Rusticus and Eleutherius, had been decapitated on the hill in the third century, and it was their martyrdom that led to the new name for the hill of "Montmartre" (the Mount of Martyrs).[9] It was also in Hilduin's writings that Saint Denis (in Latin Dionysius, first bishop of Paris) first began to be conflated with Dionysius the Areopagite (one of Saint Paul's followers from first-century Greece), and Pseudo-Dionysius (a philosopher of the late fifth to early sixth century). These references to Saint Denis, Dionysius the Areopagite, and Pseudo-Dionysius served to elevate the status of both Montmartre and the Abbey of Saint Denis (located a few miles further outside Paris), over which Hilduin presided. This status in turn led to the continued association of the Abbey of Saint Denis with the French monarchy and to its role as the final resting place of almost all French kings from Dagobert I (d. 639) onward.

In 1133 (during the reign of Louis VI) the church was refounded as a royal Benedictine convent under the leadership of one Abbess Adelaide, and on Easter Monday 1147 a new abbey church was consecrated by Pope Eugene III. The west end was dedicated to Saint Denis and the Virgin Mary, the east end to Saint Peter; shortly afterward, on the Sunday after Ascension Day, the altar of the martyrium (a smaller church lower down the hill) was dedicated to Denis, Rusticus, and Eleutherius, again by Pope Eugene. From then on the Abbey of Montmartre became an important focus of religious life in Paris, both in its own right as a site of pilgrimage to Saint Denis, patron saint of the French royal house, and as a counterpart to the Abbey of Saint Denis. In 1559 much of the abbey was destroyed by fire, remaining in virtual ruin during the Wars of Religion, which consumed France at the end of the sixteenth century; but with the return of peace on the accession of Henri IV, and with the appointment of Marie de Beauvilliers as abbess in 1598, work on the restoration of the abbey signaled a new era of influence and prosperity.[10]

It is during the rule of Beauvilliers—the period in which the music of this edition originated—that the first information concerning music at the convent becomes available. More specifically, we learn that substantial developments in the chant repertory took place around this time. In her obituary of the abbess, who died in 1657, Jacqueline Bouette de Blémur revealed that the chant at Montmartre had been either newly composed or modified at the beginning of the century:

> In the beginning Madame de Montmartre [Marie de Beauvilliers] was forced to substitute psalmody [accentuated chant] for plain chant [equal note chant] because of the appalling discord that resulted during the offices, more suitable for scandalizing than edifying the nuns. In the year 1607 Our Lord sent to her a novice from Fontevraud who sang like an angel; having received this gift, she [M. de Montmartre] taught the young nuns to imitate her [the novice], notated the choir books, and perfected the singing to its current state.[11]

This potentially fanciful account is partly confirmed in the chant books that subsequently appeared. The *Antiphonier . . . de Montmartre* (1646) and *Les Ténèbres . . . de Montmartre* (1647)[12] contain some of the earliest examples in France of newly composed *plain-chant musical*, a type of chant that reflects word stress more closely than medieval chant and which dispenses with melisma almost entirely.[13] Otherwise, little information on the musical life of the abbey during this period survives. Indeed, one of the only clues we have is Antoine Boesset's presence at the abbey and the music he composed for it, both of which suggest that, during the first half of the seventeenth century, the nuns attained significant musical skills and integrated music widely into the liturgy.

The Composer

Antoine Boesset was born in Blois in 1586.[14] During the sixteenth century the French royal family used the château there, and Boesset may well have become an *enfant de choeur* in the royal chapel, where he would have come into contact with composers Du Caurroy, Claude Le Jeune, Guillaume Costeley, and Jacques Mauduit. In 1613 he married Jeanne Guédron, daughter of the celebrated singer and composer of *airs de cour* Pierre Guédron. After serving as a singer in the royal chapel under Henri IV and as *maître des chanteurs de la chambre*, Guédron had become *maître des enfants* in 1603, and it was this position that formed part of the dowry given to Boesset on his marriage in 1613. As the son-in-law of one of the most important composers at court, Boesset's career flourished, and from 1614 his *airs* appeared in the publications of the Ballard house, both in their original polyphonic versions (4–5 voices and probably lute) and as solos with lute accompaniment.[15] In 1620 Boesset became *secretaire de la chambre du Roy*, and records indicate that by 1623 he was *surintendant de la musique du Roy*, a position he occupied in conjunction with all the others until his death in 1643.

Although Boesset is today known principally for his secular works, the music in this edition shows him to have been an important composer of sacred music for the court, both directly (the *musique de la chambre*) and indirectly (the royal Abbey of Montmartre). The duties of the *musique de la chambre* are described in the *Etat de la France* almost entirely in terms of liturgical and paraliturgical feasts, and consisted of the singing of grace at Sunday lunch, performing at the moveable altars during Corpus Christi processions, and singing at Tenebrae, royal funerals, and weddings.[16] By virtue of the royal connections of the abbey and his status as *maître de musique* to the queen (the 1133 refoundation had been under the patronage of Queen Adelaide, wife of Louis VI), Boesset was also involved in the musical provision at Montmartre. In the entry for "Montmartre" in his *Histoire et recherches des antiquités de la ville Paris*, Henri Sauval recorded that "Antoine Boesset, genius of sweet music, who was so esteemed by Louis XIII that he made him *intendant de la musique de la chambre* and that of the queen, was also interred there, to the great regret of the nuns whom he had taught to sing and who sprinkled his tomb with their tears."[17] It should thus come as no surprise that Antoine Boesset composed sacred music—his duties at his two places of employment demanded it. Yet none of his sacred music was ever published in his lifetime, and no sources unequivocally attribute any such sacred music to Antoine.[18]

TABLE 1
Works Attributed to "Boesset" in Rés. 571

Folio	Title	Scoring
1v	Domine salvum fac regem (2)	G2, G2, C1, F3, basse continue
29r–30v	Magnificat (3)	G2, G2, C2, F3, basse continue
50r–54r	*Messe à 4 du 11ᵉ mode*	G2, G2, C2, F3, basse continue
54v–55r	Salve Regina (1)	G2, C2, C3, F3, basse continue
55v–56r	Anna mater Matris	G2, G2, G2, C1, F3, basse continue
56v	De profundis	G2, G2, C2, F3
134r–139v	*Messe à 5 du 3ᵉ transposé*	G2, G2, G2, C1, F3, basse continue
170v–174r	*Messe de Boesset du Tiers*	G2, G2, C1, F3, basse continue

"Boesset" Attributions in Rés. 571

The works contained in this edition are preserved in the manuscript Paris, Bibliothèque nationale, Département de la Musique, Rés. Vᵐᵃ ms. 571 (hereafter referred to as Rés. 571), a bound volume of 239 folios containing some three hundred sacred Latin works in score. (This manuscript is often referred to as the Deslauriers manuscript, but the "Deslauriers" moniker is of little relevance and potentially misleading.) First documented as part of Sébastien de Brossard's collection and described in great detail in his *Catalogue*, Rés. 571 is the largest and one of the most significant single collections of sacred music from the seventeenth century.[19] While the vast majority of the works in Rés. 571 were transmitted anonymously, the manuscript contains eight pieces attributed simply to "Boesset," with no further clarification. Table 1 lists these works and their scoring and shows that all but two are scored for three or four high voices, bass voice, and basse continue. Another work, a version of the attributed "Domine salvum fac regem (2)" scored for mixed voices (G2, G2, C2, C3, F3) and included in the present edition as "Domine salvum fac regem (1)," is found (without attribution) on folios 175r–v, while a duplicate version of the attributed "De profundis" also appears on folio 175v. (Plate 1 shows "Domine salvum fac regem [2]" on folio 1v with the attribution to Boesset.)

Given the fame of Antoine's son Jean-Baptiste (who later inherited his father's posts and who is known to have also composed sacred music) and the widely accepted dating of the source to around 1660–80, the identity of this "Boesset" has posed a problem for scholars since the eighteenth century.[20] Brossard expressed the dilemma as follows:

> Since it was more than one hundred and twenty years since the Boessets, both father and son, held and exercised the post of *surintendant de la musique de la chambre du Roy*, it would be very difficult to determine precisely which of these Messieurs is the author of the seven works mentioned below [Brossard overlooked "Domine salvum fac regem"]. It is nevertheless quite probable that [these works] are by the one who lived around the year 1650, who was therefore a contemporary and rival of the famous Jean-Baptiste de Lully, and who died on the 27 January 1686.... He was named Jean Baptiste de Boësset, Lord of Dehaut, etc.[21]

Both Brossard's comments and the presence in the source of a part for basse continue—until now generally believed to have been introduced to France around 1650—have led to the general consensus that Jean-Baptiste composed these eight works.[22] Codicological evidence from a detailed study of the manuscript, however, points to an entirely different conclusion.

Using a process of watermark dating and watermark distribution analysis it is possible to establish the precise structure and a highly credible chronology for the copying and compilation of Rés 571. By then considering paleographical evidence and Brossard's testimony, it is also possible to deduce that one individual, André Pechon, copied the manuscript in at least three distinct stages separated by considerable periods of time.[23] Pechon was a singer and then *maître des enfants* at the royal parish church of Saint Germain l'Auxerrois (adjacent to the Louvre) from the 1620s to the 1640s, after which he took a post at Meaux Cathedral just outside Paris, where he remained until his death in the mid-1680s. He copied his collection (in score) from exemplars (presumably mostly in partbooks) he obtained from Saint Germain and, through the connection of this church to the royal court, from the repertoire of Montmartre and the *musique de la chambre*. (There was also a direct connection between Montmartre and Saint Germain, with one of the chapels in the abbey church being used for the regular celebration of mass by the clergy of Saint Germain.[24]) The earliest sections were copied in Paris, and the final section (from which much of the music in this edition is taken) was copied in the early 1680s in Meaux, though the partbook exemplars Pechon used dated from much earlier.[25]

Table 2 lists the music of this edition according to copying date and placement within the manuscript. The earliest part of the collection (fols. 127r–177v) was likely copied in the 1620s and almost certainly no later than 1632. It contains three of the works explicitly attributed to "Boesset"—*Messe à 5 du 3ᵉ transposé, Messe de Boesset du Tiers*, and "De profundis"—as well as the mixed-voice setting of "Domine salvum fac regem (1)" mentioned above. Because Jean-Baptiste was born in 1614 and occupied no official post in the 1620s, it seems inconceivable that he could have composed the music of the early part of this collection. Since Sauval's testimony places Antoine Boesset at Montmartre, and since these works are scored

TABLE 2
Copying Phases of Boesset's Music in Rés. 571

Folio	Title	Part: Number in Edition*
Phase 1: 1632 (possibly as early as the 1620s)		
134v–139v	*Messe à 5 du 3ᵉ transposé*	2
144v	Quam pulchra es	1:53
149v–150v	Regina caeli (1)	1:26
152r–v	Ave Maria (1)	1:3
153r–v	Sancta Maria	1:33
153v–154r	Ave Maria (2)	1:4
154v–155v	Libera me	2:18
155v–156v	Magnificat (1)	2:1
157r–158r	Magnificat (2)	2:2
158r–160r	Dixit Dominus	2:10
160r–161r	Laudate pueri (1)	2:13
161v–162v	Laetatus sum	2:12
165v	Ecce panis Angelorum	1:15
165v–167r	Fons aquae vivae	1:16
169v	Kyrie	2:15
169v–170r	Sanctus, Benedictus	2:16
170v	Agnus Dei	2:17
170v–174r	*Messe de Boesset du Tiers*	2
175r–v	Domine salvum fac regem (1)	1:10
177v	Pie Jesu	2:19
Phase 2: 1638–41		
29r–30v	Magnificat (3)	2:3
50r–54r	*Messe à 4 du 11ᵉ mode*	2
54v–55r	Salve Regina (1)	1:30
55v–56r	Anna mater Matris	1:2
1v	Domine salvum fac regem (2)	1:11
Phase 3: 1682		
178r–180r	Te Deum (1)	2:7
180r–181v	Te Deum (2)	2:8
181v–182r	Popule meus	1:24
182v–183r	Ecce quam bonum	2:11
187r–v	Veni Creator Spiritus	1:54
187v–188r	Ave per cor suavissimum Jesu	1:5
188v	Tu es Petrus	1:34
189r–190r	Tu es vas electionis	1:35
190r–191v	Beatus vir	2:9
191v–192v	Magnificat (4)	2:4
192v–193v	Magnificat (5)	2:5
193v	Quam pulchra es (alternative refrain)	1:53a
193v–194r	O quam suavis	1:22
194r–v	O salutaris hostia	1:50
194v–195r	Ave salus mundi	1:7
195r–v	O sacrum convivium	1:23
195v–196r	O crux ave	1:19
196r–v	Veni Sancte Spiritus	1:36
196v–197r	Domine salvum fac regem (3)	1:12
197r	Domine salvum fac regem (4)	1:13
197v–198r	Dionysii martyris	1:46
198r–v	Pretiosus Domini Dionysius	1:25
198v–199r	Iste Confessor	1:47
199r	Christe redemptor omnium, Conserva	1:43
199v–200r	Alma Redemptoris Mater	1:1
200r–v	Ave Regina caelorum	1:6
200v–201v	Salve Regina (2)	1:31

TABLE 2 continued

Folio	Title	Part: Number in Edition*
201v–202r	Salve Regina (3)	1:32
202v–203r	Regina caeli (2)	1:27
203r–v	Duo seraphim (with alternative opening)	1:14
204r–v	Hic est beatissimus	1:17
204v–205v	O athletum invictissimum	1:18
205v–206v	O Doctor optime	1:20
206v–207r	O Pastor aeterne	1:21
207r–v	Ave virginum gemma Catharina	1:8
207v	O gloriosae virgines	1:49
208r–v	Benedicimus te	1:9
208v–209r	Regnum mundi	1:29
209r–210v	Alleluja. O filii et filiae	1:39
210v–211r	Vir Domini Benedictus	1:37
211r	Christe redemptor omnium, Ex Patre	1:44
211v	Ad caenam Agni	1:38
211v–212r	Pange lingua . . . Corporis	1:51
212v–213r	Ave maris stella	1:41
213r–v	Aurea luce	1:40
213v–214r	Claris conjubila	1:45
214r–v	Ave mater pia	1:42
214v–215r	Pange lingua . . . Certaminis	1:52
217r	Jesu, nostra redemptio	1:48
219v–221r	Laudate pueri (2)	2:14
221r–221v	Regina caeli (3)	1:28
221v–223r	Magnificat (6)	2:6

*Masses appear without numbers at the end of part 2.

for multiple high voices, it seems reasonable to propose that the high-voice settings were composed by Antoine for Montmartre, with Boesset himself possibly singing the bass part—a scenario Henri Quittard had considered as a possibility a century ago.[26]

The next part of the collection (fols. 29r–56v and fol. 1v) was copied around 1638–41 and contains the motet "Anna mater Matris" (again for high voices), whose text relates the story of Saint Anne, mother of the Virgin Mary and patron saint of childbirth. In 1638 Louis XIII's queen and namesake of the saint, Anne of Austria, had finally given birth to the future Louis XIV, and it seems clear that this piece was intended to celebrate the event. Since Antoine Boesset was by now *maître de musique* to the queen, and since Montmartre also fell under her patronage, this work too can almost certainly be attributed to Antoine.[27] Although there is no additional indisputable evidence to attribute the other "Boesset" works from the same part of the collection (Magnificat [3], *Messe à 4 du 11ᵉ mode,* and Salve regina [1]) to Antoine, Jean-Baptiste remains an implausible candidate, having had no connection to Montmartre, no official position at court, and no apparent connection to Pechon.

By virtue of their liturgical function and the performance forces they require, the works for high voices thus far attributed to Antoine would have been entirely appropriate for performance at Montmartre. Yet little about these compositions locates them definitively at that particular abbey. By contrast, a stylistically unified group of works elsewhere in the source (fols. 177v–229v), copied in the final episode around 1682, shows clear and unambiguous connections to the abbey and undoubtedly served as its liturgical repertory. This connection is illustrated first in the martyrology of some of these works shown in table 3. Montmartre was a shrine to Saint Denis, with the abbey church being dedicated to Saint Peter and its apsidal chapel to Saint Catherine. Saint Paul is associated with Dionysius the Areopagite, while Saint Ursula was central to the abbey's foundation.[28] And as one would expect from a repertory composed for a Benedictine abbey, a number of pieces are provided for celebrating the important feasts relating to St. Benedict.

The presence of alternatim fragments of chant corresponding to the unique chants composed for Montmartre in the early years of the seventeenth century also link these works to the abbey. The responsory for the Ceremony of the Vesture of Novices, "Regnum mundi," for example, sets the novice's chant as a soprano solo (see example 1 and the opening of "Regnum mundi"), while Magnificat (1) is provided in the source with two fragments of chant, one copied in the 1620s, one in the 1680s. Although both fragments are slight variants of each

Example 1. Response "Regnum mundi" (*Antiphonier . . . de Montmartre*, 521).

Re-gnum mun-di et om- nem or-na-tum sae-cu- li con-tem-psi.

TABLE 3
Martyrology of Late-Copied Repertoire in Rés. 571

Martyr	Feast Day	Title	Folio	Text Type
St. Peter	January 18	Tu es Petrus	188v	offertory
St. Denis	October 9	Dionysii martyris	197v–198r	hymn
		Pretiosus Domini Dionysius	198r–v	response
St. Peter and St. Paul	June 29	Aurea luce	213r–v	hymn
St. Catherine	November 25	Ave virginum gemma Catharina	207r–v	antiphon
St. Benedict	March 21 (commemoration)	Vir Domini Benedictus	210v–211r	antiphon
	July 11 (translation)	Claris conjubila	213v–214r	hymn
St. Ursula	October 21	Pange lingua . . . Certaminis	214v–215r	hymn

other, both clearly relate closely to the version published in 1646 in the *Antiphonier . . . de Montmartre* (see plates 2, 3, and 4). And for the alternatim hymn settings, the source provides rhythmicized versions of the *plain-chant musical* hymn melodies, most of which are again melodically concordant with the distinctive melodies that appear uniquely in the *Antiphonier . . . de Montmartre* (see plate 4).

Although the final section of the manuscript was copied in the 1680s, the connection between these late-copied works and the Montmartre chants in fact provides a much earlier *terminus ante quem* for their composition. While several of these melodies are identical to those in the *Antiphonier . . . de Montmartre,* a significant number are either slight variants or unrelated to the published chants. If the composer of this music had been working after 1646, we would expect him to have used the versions of these chants published in the *Antiphonier . . . de Montmartre.* Yet the fact that he used variants suggests that he was he was working before 1646—that is, before the chant repertory was standardized in the printed edition.

Other evidence further suggests that the music of this late-copied section was composed in the early, rather than middle, decades of the seventeenth century. Several of the high-voice works exist in parallel versions for mixed voices, obviously intended for use in the *musique de la chambre.* Two of these parallel versions ("Quam pulchra es" and "Regina caeli [1]") are found in the earliest part of the collection (fols. 127–177) and can thus be dated to the 1620s, confirming that pieces preserved in the late-copied section also originated in the 1620s. Add to this the striking stylistic cohesiveness of all these works and their connections to the works attributed in the source to "Boesset" (now established as Antoine), and the authorship seems clear. Well-acquainted with Antoine Boesset in the 1630s and 1640s, Pechon copied a repertoire he had collected into Rés. 571 as the final act of a long-time music collector organizing and preserving this music for posterity. Although Antoine's sacred music was now worlds away from the motets for conventual use by Guillaume-Gabriel Nivers and Nicolas Lebègue appearing around this time, Pechon obviously considered it worth preserving. Indeed, Antoine Boesset's reputation as a composer lasted well into the eighteenth century. If further evidence was needed in establishing both Antoine's fame and his superiority over his son Jean-Baptiste, Jean Laurent le Cerf de la Viéville's testimony from the first decade of the eighteenth century certainly accounts for Pechon's continued interest in his long-departed acquaintance Antoine:

> The Boesset whom you knew was Boesset the younger, a mediocre musician. Everything of quality under that name [Boesset] is by his father, who is called old Boesset, and about whom I have always spoken. It was the father whom Lully esteemed, a man whose memory will be never forgotten by musicians.[29]

The Music of the Edition

Rés. 571 contains all of Boesset's extant music for the Royal Abbey of Montmartre and the *chambre* of Louis XIII. Preserved in versions requiring several female voices but only one male voice (typically using the clefs G2, G2, G2, C1, F3 and supported by basse continue), the majority of the works were composed for Montmartre. These works indicate a widespread use of music throughout the liturgy and include three complete mass ordinary settings (two through-composed and one alternatim), together with a number of individual mass ordinary and requiem movements. In addition, the manuscript contains several through-composed and alternatim Magnificats (three of them based on the unique Montmartre chant repertory), as well as settings of other canticles (Nunc dimittis and Te Deum) and psalms for the divine offices ("Laudate pueri," "Dixit Dominus," and "Beatus vir"). Boesset also set a number of alternatim hymns, most of them based on the unique melodies preserved in the *Antiphonier . . . de Montmartre* and also recorded in a section devoted to chant in the source (see plate 4). Following the rhythmic pattern of the polyphonic settings, the hymn melodies are also given a corresponding rhythm: triple-meter polyphonic settings are provided with triple-meter chant melodies, resulting in works of a unique hybrid character.

For more specific liturgical celebrations, Boesset composed a number of works for both Salut (the office of the Benediction of the Blessed Sacrament) and the Ceremony of the Vesture of Novices. A confraternity of Saint Denis had been founded at the abbey in 1623, and its statutes required the celebration of Salut each Thursday.[30] The hymn "Pange lingua . . . Corporis" is explicitly mentioned in the order, as is "Alleluja. O filii et filiae" (a song of rejoicing for Easter), and other Eucharistic works such as "O quam suavis," "O salutaris hostia," "Ave salus mundi," and "O sacrum convivium" may also have been used. And for the elaborate Ceremony of the Vesture of Novices, Boesset set five items.[31] "Veni Creator Spiritus" (sung at the end of mass immediately preceding the ceremony) was set as an alternatim hymn based on the chant provided in the *Antiphonier . . . de Montmartre*. The processional hymn "O gloriosa domina" was set using "Quam pulchra es" as a refrain, a feature often found in processional hymns. A setting of the hymn verse "O crux ave" would have been performed as the procession turned to face the cross, while the psalm "Ecce quam bonum" was set in the responsorial manner specified in the *Antiphonier . . . de Montmartre*. Finally, the responsory "Regnum mundi" quotes the Montmartre chant in its opening solo, surely intended to be sung by the novice herself.

Alongside his activities at Montmartre, as *surintendant de la musique* to Louis XIII Boesset was also responsible for the provision of devotional music for performance in the small chapels and elsewhere in the Louvre. Four works in this edition, typically scored for G2, C2, C3, C4, F3, and basse continue (and thus suitable for the male voices available in the *chambre*), were composed or adapted for this purpose: "Quam pulchra es," "Regina caeli (1)," "Ave Maria (1)," and "Domine salvum fac regem (1)." All four also exist in alternative versions for high voices, bass, and basse continue, which were intended for use at Montmartre, although not all needed to be modified extensively; in the case of "Quam pulchra es," the verse settings could be performed by either ensemble, while the refrains exist in two versions—one for high voices, the other for mixed. The other works were modified to varying degrees for the two institutions: while "Regina caeli (1)" and "Domine salvum fac regem (1)" were simply rescorings or "parallel" versions, "Ave Maria (1)" was more extensively altered. (We have no way of knowing which of these paired versions was the "original.") Three other works, "Salve regina (1)," "Laudate Pueri (2)" and "Regina caeli (3)" only exist in one version, but their scoring (G2, C2, C3, F3) allowed them to be performed in both institutions by either ensemble. The liturgical function of all these works would also have changed with the venue of their performance. "Domine salvum fac regem," in particular, had two clearly defined functions: one as an appendage to the mass (at Montmartre), another as a royal ceremonial work (at court).[32]

Boesset's sacred music shows a remarkably homogeneous style that is in many respects similar to that found in his secular works. A hallmark of Boesset's polyphonic *airs de cour* is a mosaic of changing scorings, with solos and duets rapidly alternating both with each other and with full sections. This procedure appears throughout Boesset's sacred works, as does the occasional alternation of duple and triple meter also found in the airs. Boesset makes more frequent use of imitation in his sacred works than in the airs, but this procedure is something we would probably expect; certainly throughout the seventeenth and eighteenth centuries, imitative polyphony was seen as the hallmark of church music, and Boesset would have been doing no more than using an appropriate compositional convention. But in contrast to the austere contemporary settings of Bournonville and d'Ambleville, this music has great charm, and viewed alongside the later works in Dumont's 1652 *Cantica sacra*, these works illustrate a compositional practice much more closely allied with pure French aesthetic ideals, rather than one tinged with Italianisms. Boesset's sacred music is thus clearly a new and critical factor that we must take into account when considering the development of French music in the *grand siècle*.

Notes on Performance

Performing Ensemble

Although the source lacks voice designations, the scoring of these works and their institutional connections make it possible to determine who would have originally performed this music. The vocal ensemble available in the *musique de la chambre* consisted of three boys singing in unison and up to five men. The part written in C3 clef would have been taken by a man ("haute-taille" or high tenor), as would the parts in C4 ("taille" or tenor/baritone) and F clefs ("basse" or bass).[33] For the works composed for Montmartre, the parts written in G2, C1, C2, and C3 clef would have been sung by women (sopranos and mezzo-sopranos or contraltos in today's terms). The bass voice part may have been sung by Boesset himself or another male singer, though, apart from special occasions, it may have simply been omitted. (Since the bass voice merely doubles the basse continue line, performance without it would have been completely viable.) Although it might seem unusual for a man to participate in the convent's music making, the royal status of the abbey allowed exceptions to be made to the usual rules governing contact with men; evidence from later in the century certainly points to men performing in the church,[34] and Sauval's testimony quoted above confirms contact between Boesset and the nuns.

We have no information as to whether this music was performed by a small ensemble or by large numbers of nuns singing together. However, the opening phrase of "Regnum mundi" would surely have been sung by a soloist, possibly the novice herself, and several other pieces imply the use of a soloist reinforced by the choir in the full sections (e.g. "Sancta Maria," "Tu es Petrus," and "Tu es vas electionis"). The chant portions of the alternatim works (the *Messe de Boesset du Tiers*, three Magnificats, a Te Deum, and several hymns) would probably have been performed by all the nuns, the designation "Le Choeur" used in the source probably referring to the location in the abbey church where the nuns celebrated the liturgy (the choir) rather than the vocal ensemble that sang the polyphony. (It should of course be remembered that all the nuns would have actively participated in all the chant portions of the liturgy.)

The works preserved in this manuscript make use of the basse continue at least twenty years before Dumont's

Cantica sacra, generally recognized as the first appearance in France of the technique in sacred music.[35] At Montmartre, the basse continue was probably realized by organ alone (in the late-copied body of work, this part is marked "Org.") or with organ and bass viol (the part for the *Messe à 4 du 11ᵉ mode* is marked "basse continue" and "viole"). By contrast, the basse continue of the *musique de la chambre* ensemble consisted of bass viol, harpsichord, and lute.[36] The basse continue part lacks figures throughout; suggestions for its realization may be found in Denis Delair's *Traité d'accompagnement* (1690), the earliest relevant French treatise on the subject.[37]

Chant and Rhythm

The music of this edition was composed and copied during a period in which French theorists and performers grappled with a number of different approaches to the rhythmic notation and performance of chant, all of which should be seen in the context of wider humanist reforms in which text declamation and clarity became paramount. In France the earliest stages of the reform (generally called *plain-chant musical*) are generally associated with Oratorians and Pierre Bourgoing's *Brevis psalmodiae ratio* (1634), although the chant associated with Montmartre can now also be dated to the same period or earlier. For that reason, it is not yet clear exactly how this chant is to be performed, although Pierre-Benoît de Jumilhac's slightly later *Science et pratique du plain-chant* (1673) provides some guidance in determining the extent to which these chants should be performed in rhythm. (For further discussion of the chant transcriptions, see the critical report.) The rhythmicized chant melodies that Boesset provided for the alternatim hymns should be performed in the ternary meter in which they are notated, a practice Jumilhac called *chant metrique*.[38] By contrast, the alternatim Magnificat and Te Deum chant versets should be performed in *chant rhythmique,* a declamatory performance style that reflects word accentuation by slightly lengthening and stressing important syllables. (The sections of fauxbourdon in Te Deum [2] should also be performed in this way.) While the Magnificat chant versets are notated using black breves and semibreves in the *Antiphonier . . . de Montmartre,* these rhythmic durations should be interpreted as a flexible lengthening or shortening of notes, rather than according to a strict system in which a breve is twice as long as a semibreve. For the mass ordinary movements, Jumilhac specified that the chants were to be performed in *plain chant,* i.e. generally obeying the "equal note" principle. Yet Pechon's notation and the analogous sections of the *Antiphonier . . . de Montmartre* imply that even in *plain chant* not all notes were to be performed exactly equally, and that semibreves (generally associated with weak syllables) should be performed shorter than breves. This style of performance would be in accord with that suggested by Bourgoing.[39]

Meter

The early and mid-seventeenth century was a period of transition with respect to the notation of meter. Although the fixed tactus of the Renaissance was no longer observed, and although composers now generally used smaller note values than they had before, vestiges of Renaissance theories of proportion—including passages of coloration and symbols such as ⌽ and ₵3—were still occasionally found. Yet by Boesset's time this notation was rarely used in any sort of systematic manner. More common in the music of this edition are the apparently straightforward signs C, ₵, 2, and 3, but even these carry different meanings depending on whether they are interpreted as indicators of proportional relationships, as time signatures (in the modern sense), or as indicators of tempo. Complicating matters further, the music of this edition occasionally uses these signs in several ways simultaneously, posing considerable interpretive challenges to the modern performer. A few general performance guidelines are offered here, but performers are urged to experiment in order to arrive at an interpretation that makes musical and historical sense.

For the music of this edition, the signs C and ₵ should rarely be interpreted in a strict proportional sense (in which ₵ was twice as fast as C). Rather, they signal which note value should receive the beat (the quarter note or half note, respectively) and serve as tempo indications, with ₵ being somewhat faster than C.[40] Performers should therefore interpret works alternating between C and ₵ through shifts in tempo, rather than by doubling or halving note values. Works in ₵ could include either four half notes per measure (seen principally in the early-copied works), two half notes per measure, or a fluctuation between the two. Neither should the signs 2 and 3 generally be interpreted as proportional relationships, since part of the compositional aesthetic of the 1620s through the 1640s was a metrical freedom often expressed in alternating groupings of two and three. Boesset's contemporary *airs de cour* and the hymns of this edition make frequent use of this practice, and the alternation between 2 and 3 is best understood in the context of a musical practice still influenced by the interest in ancient poetic meters exemplified in the *musique mesurée* of the late sixteenth century. Thus, these symbols do not indicate proportional relationships as we might expect for this time; rather, the 2 and 3 represent metrical groupings in which the note value remains constant, rather than the tactus.[41] Performers should therefore assume a system of equivalency in which the quarter note equals quarter note (or half note equals half note), unless otherwise indicated by a metrical equivalency above the staff.

Notes

1. In contrast to other European countries, where numerous independent music publishers generally vied with each other for business, in France the Le Roy and Ballard company (later just Ballard) held a virtual monopoly on music publishing from the mid-sixteenth century until the mid-seventeenth century and remained dominant into the eighteenth century. During the reign of Louis XIII, Robert Ballard II focused the company's output on *airs de cour,* to the almost complete exclusion of Latin sacred music.

2. Eustache du Caurroy, *Preces ecclesiastiae ad numeros musices redactae* (Paris: P. Ballard, 1609); Jean de Bournonville, *Octo cantica Virginis matris* (Paris: P. Ballard, 1612 and 1625); Charles d'Ambleville, *Harmonia sacra seu vesperae in dies tum dominicos, tum festos totius anni, una cum missa ac litaniis beatae virginis cum quatuor vocibus* (Paris: P. Ballard, 1636); *Harmonia sacra seu vesperae in dies tum dominicos, tum festos totius anni, una cum missa ac litaniis beatae virginis cum sex vocibus* (Paris: P. Ballard, 1636); and Nicolas Formé, *Musica simplex quatuor vocum* (Paris: P. Ballard, 1638).

3. Henri Frémart's eight masses for four, five, and six voices were probably written in the 1630s but were published in Paris between 1642 and 1645. A modern edition is available in Henri Frémart, *Oeuvres complètes,* ed. Inge Forst, Patrimoine musical français, series I (Anthologies), Musique des maîtrises de France, vol. 5 (Versailles: Centre de Musique Baroque de Versailles, 2003).

4. Nicolas Formé, *Le Cantique de la Vierge Marie selon les Tons ou Modes usités en l'église,* manuscript, Paris, Bibliothèque nationale, MS fonds français 1870.

5. Nicolas Formé, *Missa aeternae Henrici Magni* (Paris: P. Ballard, 1638). Formé's setting makes use of two unequal choirs, an arrangement that prefigures that of the *grand motet.*

6. For a general summary of sacred music in France in the seventeenth century, see Denise Launay, *La musique religieuse en France du Concile de Trente à 1804* (Paris: Societe française de musicologie, Éditions Klincksieck, 1993).

7. All seventeenth-century accounts use the orthography "Boesset." It is only in the eighteenth century that "Boësset" came into common usage.

8. This account of the foundation of Montmartre is based on Abbé LeBeuf, *Histoire de la ville et de tout le diocese de Paris* (Paris: Fechoz and Letouzey, 1883), 440–55. The cult of Saint Denis is explored in Sumner McKnight Crosby, *The Abbey of St. Denis: 475–1122* (New Haven, Conn.: Yale University Press, 1942), 41–52.

9. Despite having his head cut off, Denis supposedly continued out of Paris to the spot where the Abbey of Saint Denis now stands. As Hilduin put it, after being decapitated, Denis "took up his own head from the hill where it had been removed, and carried it about two miles to the place which God had chosen for him to lay his body, all the time praising God in sweet hymns of praise." Quoted in Léon Levillain, "Études sur l'Abbaye de Saint-Denis a l'époque mérovingienne," *Bibliothèque de l'École des Chartes* 80 (1921): 49. All translations are by the author.

10. On 11 July 1611, builders making repairs to the martyrium discovered an underground stairway that led to an ancient crypt said to have been sanctified by Saint Denis himself. Marie de Medici and more than sixty thousand people are said to have visited the site. So many charitable donations were made that the martyrium was enlarged and a substantial new church and dependent priory built. Henri Sauval, *Histoire et recherches des antiquités de la ville de Paris,* 3 vols. (Paris: Moette, 1724; reprint, Westmead: Gregg International, 1984), 1:352. Citations are to the 1724 edition.

11. "Madame de Montmartre avoit esté contrainte en ces commencemens de substituer la psalmodie en la place du plein chant, à cause de l'effroyable desaccord qui se commettoit à l'Office, bien plus propre à scandalizer qu'à edifier les assistans. Nostre Seigneur luy envoye en six cens sept une Novice de Fontevraud, qui chantoit comme une Ange, laquelle s'estant donnée à elle, apprit à la jeunesse à l'imiter; elle notta les livres du choeur, & mit la chant en la perfection où il est maintenant." Jacqueline Bouette de Blémur, *L'année bénédictine,* 7 vols. (Paris: Billaine, 1667), 3:27.

12. *Antiphonier Bénédictin pour les réligieuses du Royal et célèbre monastère de Montmartre* (Paris: L. Sevestre, 1646), and *Les Ténèbres de la Semaine Sainte pour les religieuses de Montmartre* (Paris: L. Sevestre, 1647).

13. If Blémur's account is reliable, this chant predates the earliest known example of *plain-chant musical,* that in François Bourgoing, *Brevis psalmodiae ratio* (Paris: P. Ballard, 1634). The origins of *plain-chant musical* are discussed in Philippe Vendrix, "Pour les grands et les autres: la réforme oratorienne du plain-chant," in *Plain-chant et liturgie en France au XVIIe siècle,* ed. Jean Duron, 87–96 (Versailles: Centre de Musique Baroque de Versailles, 1997).

14. Biographical information is taken from Maurice Cauchie, "La dynastie des Boessets," *Revue de musicologie* 4 (1920): 13–26; and Norbert Dufourcq, "Jean-Baptiste de Boësset (1615–1685)," *La vie musicale en France sous les rois Bourbons* series 1, no. 8 (1962): 9–12.

15. In 1606 Pierre Ballard inherited his father Robert's business and began issuing volumes of *airs de cour* in four- and five-voice versions under the generic title *Airs à quatre de différents autheurs.* In 1608 Gabriel Bataille, who had succeeded Adrian Le Roy as court lutenist, was commissioned to provide lute accompaniments for six volumes of solo-voice versions of *airs de cour* that appeared between 1608 and 1615 under the generic title *Airs de cour de différents autheurs mis en tablature de luth par Gabrielle Bataille.* After the 1615 volumes (volumes seven and eight) were published, Ballard himself took over this task, with successive volumes entitled *Airs de cour de différents autheurs mis en tablature de luth par eux-mesmes.* Volumes nine and later of the series had lute intabulations by Boesset. Volume eleven of this series, though not indicated as such, contained exclusively works by Boesset, while volumes twelve (which was called *Airs de cour mis en tablature de la Luth par Anthoine Boesset* [1624]) and later were also dedicated solely to Boesset's works. Another series of anthologies, presenting just the vocal part without accompaniment, was also issued in eight volumnes as *Airs de différents autheurs* (1615–28). Finally, Boesset also had his own series of *Airs de cour à quatre & cinq parties,* which ran to nine volumes between 1617 and 1642.

16. *L'État de la France* (Paris: Guignard, 1669), 107. Although this source was later published almost annually, no copies exist for the reign of Louis XIII. Nevertheless, the duties of the various parts of the royal household barely changed over centuries.

17. "De nos jours, Antoine Boësset, le genie de la Musique douce, & si estimé de Louis XIII, qu'il le fit Intendant de la Musique de sa Chambre & de celle de la Reine, y été aussi enterré, au grand regret des Religieuses, à qui avoit appris à chanter, & qui arroserent son tombeau de leurs larmes." See Sauval, *Histoire,* 1:353. The section on Parisian churches was actually written by Jean Launoi in the mid- to late seventeenth century. Sauval's evidence is thus closer to the events recorded than the date of publication would suggest. This general piece of evidence is supported by documentary proof that, shortly after Antoine's death, his widow was granted permission to make alterations to a chapel in the abbey church, presumably

the chapel in which his tomb lay. A.N. Minutier central XX.252 (14 July 1644), reproduced in Madeleine Jurgens, *Documents du minutier central concernant l'histoire de la musique (1600–1650)*, 2 vols. (Paris: S.E.V.P.E.N., 1967), 2:137.

18. It should be mentioned, however, that the prefaces to Boesset's seventh (1630) and ninth (1642) books of *airs de cour* allude to him as a composer of sacred music.

19. Sébastien de Brossard, *Catalogue des livres de musique theoretique et prattique, vocalle et instrumentalle, tant imprimée que manuscripte* (Paris, Bibliothéque nationale, Rés. Vm^8 20); modern edition, Yolande de Brossard, ed., *La collection Sebastien de Brossard, 1655–1730: Catalogue* (Paris: Bibliotheque nationale de France, 1994).

20. Jean-Baptiste was a colleague and contemporary of Jean-Baptiste Lully. Literary evidence suggests that in addition to his duties composing *airs* for court, he was also admired for his sacred music: "The music of the Chapel worthy of immortal glory and also that of the *chambre* . . . charmed all ears beginning with a motet composed by the said Boisset whereby all the assembled company admired his divine genius." See Jean Loret, *La muze historique* (Paris: Chenault, 1650–1665), book 14, letter 3 (20 January 1663), page 9.

21. See Brossard, *Catalogue*, 351; and Brossard, *La collection*, 476.

22. For example, these works are attributed to Jean-Baptiste in the *New Grove Dictionary of Music and Musicians*, 2nd ed., s.v. "Boesset, Jean-Baptiste" (p. 784), by Austin B. Caswell and Georgie Durosoir.

23. For a fuller explanation of the attribution to Antoine Boesset, see Peter Bennett, *Sacred Repertories in Paris Under Louis XIII: Paris, Bibliothèque nationale de France MS V^{ma} Rés. 571*, Royal Musical Association Monographs 17 (Farnham, U.K.: Ashgate, 2009), 13–67; and Bennett, "Antoine Boësset's Sacred Music for the Royal Abbey of Montmartre: Newly Identified Polyphony and plain-chant musical from the 'Deslauriers' Manuscript (F-Pn V^{ma} ms. rés. 571)," *Revue de musicologie* 91 (2005): 322–67. The only previous study of the manuscript appeared in the introduction to Denise Launay, *Anthologie du motet latin polyphonique en France (1609–1661)* (Paris: Heugel, 1963), xliii–xlv.

24. A document preserved in Paris, Archives nationales de France, L. 1030, records the arrangement by which the clergy of Saint Germain were allowed to use the chapel of Saint Leuffroy.

25. For the identification of Pechon as scribe, see Bennett, *Sacred Repertories*, 55–67. By virtue of the very long period over which the scribe of the manuscript worked (around sixty years) and evidence from Brossard and elsewhere, André Pechon is the only plausible candidate. Copying errors such as the horizontal displacement of parts by half a measure suggest individual parts as the copying exemplar.

26. Henri Quittard, *Un musicien en France au XVIIe siecle: Henry Du Mont* (Paris: Mercure de France, 1906; reprint, Geneva: Minkoff, 1973), 35.

27. Other works in praise of Anne were published in the same year. For example, an *air* for dessus et basse "Sur la naissance de Monsieur le Dauphin" appeared in Antoine Parran, *Traite de la musique théorique et pratique, contenant les préceptes de la composition* (Paris: P. Ballard, 1639; reprint, Geneva: Minkoff, 1973).

28. Sauval, *Histoire*, 1:351.

29. Jean Laurent le Cerf de la Viéville, *Comparaison de la musique italienne, et de la musique françoise*, 2 vols. (Brussels: François Foppens, 1705; reprint, Geneva: Minkoff, 1972), 2:123–4. Citation is to the 1705 publication.

30. Information on the foundation of the confraternity and its rite is preserved in Pierre de Sainte-Catherine, *Cérémonial monastique des religieuses de l'abbaye royale de Montmartre* (Paris: B. & M. Vitré, 1669).

31. Although no order for the ceremony local to Montmartre survives, a contemporary order from the Benedictine Abbey of Montier-Villiers indicates the musical items required. *Cérémonial des religieuses de l'Abbaye de N. Dame de Montier-Villiers, Ordre de sainct Benoit* (Paris: P. Chevalier, 1626). For a full discussion of the ceremony see Bennett, *Sacred Repertories*, 148–56.

32. These settings of "Domine salvum fac regem" are the earliest to use the text in this form, which later became a standard part of the mass at Versailles.

33. This ensemble remained unchanged throughout the reign of Louis XIII and into the reign of Louis XIV. See *Musique de la chambre du Roi* (1631), Paris, Archives nationales de France, Z^{1a} 472.

34. Later in the century numerous accounts record male involvement in music making at the abbey. For example, for the confirmation as abbess of Françoise-Renée de Lorraine in 1657, Loret reports that "many psalms, motets, *cantiques* were sung by the musicians . . . among forty who sang, Berthod and Le-Gros." (Berthod and Le-Gros were singers in the Chapelle Royale.) See Loret, *La muze historique*, book 8, letter 20 (26 May 1657), page 75.

35. The indication for basse continue appeared just once in Boesset's published polyphonic *airs* editions, with the direction "basse continue pour les instruments" for *Ayme moy, Cloris*, found in the *VIIe Livre d'airs de cour à quatre & cinq parties* (Paris: P. Ballard, 1630). In Boesset's *IIe Livre d'airs de cour à quatre & cinq parties* (Paris: P. Ballard, 1620) we find the direction "basse pour les luthes" for the air *A ce coup, valeureux de Mars*. Despite the paucity of explicit indications, there is no reason to suppose that, in practice, the lutenist (who would not have been provided with an intabulated setting in the polyphonic edition) did not play a basse continue part.

36. See *Musique de la chambre du Roi*.

37. Denis Delair, *Traite d'accompagnement pour le theorbe et le clavessin* (Paris, 1690).

38. See Pierre-Benoît de Jumilhac, *La science et la pratique du plain-chant* (Paris: L. Bilaine, 1673), 147–65. The practice of performing hymn melodies in meter appears to have originated in the Renaissance. See Richard Sherr, "The Performance of Chant in the Renaissance and its Interactions with Polyphony," in *Plainsong in the Age of Polyphony*, ed. Thomas Kelly (Cambridge: Cambridge University Press, 1992), 189–94.

39. F. Bourgoing, *Brevis psalmodiae ratio*.

40. For more on interpretations of C and ¢ during this period, see George Houle, *Meter in Music, 1600–1800: Performance, Perception, and Notation* (Bloomington: Indiana University Press, 1987), 14–17.

41. A detailed treatment of this subject can be found in Denise Launay, "Les rapports de tempo entre mesures binaires et mesures ternaires dans la musique française (1600–1650)," *Fontes artis musicae* 12 (1965): 166–94.

Texts and Translations

Texts follow capitalization and punctuation of the *Liber Usualis* and the *Antiphonale Monasticum*. References to the biblical origins or liturgical function of the texts appear in the comments below. All translations are by the editor; translations have been rendered as literally as possible in order to help performers understand individual words from the Latin texts.

Motets

1. *Alma Redemptoris Mater*

Alma Redemptoris Mater, quae pervia caeli porta manes,
Et stella maris, succurre cadenti surgere qui curat populo:
Tu quae genuisti, natura mirante, tuum sanctum Genitorem:
Virgo prius ac posterius, Gabrielis ab ore sumens illud Ave, peccatorum miserere.

Loving Mother of our Redeemer, who remains a gateway to heaven,
and star of the sea, succor the fallen people, who strive to rise:
You who brought forth, by marvelous birth, your own holy Creator:
Virgin before and after, receiving that "Ave" from the mouth of Gabriel, have mercy on sinners.

Comment. Marian antiphon.

2. *Anna mater Matris*

Anna mater Matris redemptoris nostri, Anna matrona nobillissima, quae jam regnat cum angelis, coronata in gloria, ibi nostri memor esto. O Anna sanctissima, funde preces pro nobis, ut possimus illic tuo sociari collegio.

Anne, mother of the Mother of our Redeemer, Anne, most noble lady, who now reigns with the angels, crowned in glory, be mindful of us there. O Anne most holy, pray for us, that we might be united there with your assembly.

Comment. Unidentified text in praise of St. Anne.

3–4. *Ave Maria*

Ave Maria, gratia plena, Dominus tecum, benedicta tu in mulieribus, et benedictus fructus ventris tui, Jesus.

Sancta Maria, Mater Dei, ora pro nobis peccatoribus, nunc et in hora mortis nostrae. Amen.

Hail Mary, full of grace, the Lord is with you, blessed are you among women, and blessed is the fruit of your womb, Jesus.

Holy Mary, Mother of God, pray for us sinners, now and at the hour of our death. Amen.

Comment. Marian antiphon.

5. *Ave per cor suavissimum Jesu*

Ave per cor suavissimum Jesu, o beata virgo Gertrudis, Paraclitus deliciarum Christi. Gaudeo de tua gloria et laudo Deum: Illicque pro te offero dulcissimum cor Jesu. Eja ergo sponsa Christi gloriosa. Ora pro nobis Dominum ut omnino fiamus secundum cor Dei. Amen.

Hail, through the most sweet heart of Jesus, O blessed virgin Gertrude, Paraclete of Christ's delight. I rejoice in your glory and I praise God: And I offer the most sweet heart of Jesus for you. Now, glorious bride of Christ. Pray for us to the Lord, that we will be made according to the heart of God. Amen.

Comment. Unidentified text, Feast of Saint Gertrude.

6. *Ave Regina caelorum*

Ave Regina caelorum,	Hail Queen of Heaven,
Ave Domina Angelorum:	hail Mistress of Angels;
Salve radix, salve porta,	hail root, hail gate,
Ex qua mundo lux est orta:	from whom light rose over the earth;
Gaude Virgo gloriosa,	rejoice glorious Virgin,
Super omnes speciosa:	beautiful above all others;
Vale, o valde decora,	farewell, O most noble one,
Et pro nobis Christum exora.	and pray to Christ for us.

Comment.   Marian antiphon.

7. *Ave salus mundi*

Ave salus mundi, Verbum patris, hostia sacra, Vera viva caro, Deitas integra, verus homo: Corpus Domini nostri Jesu Christi qui me formasti, tu miserere mei. Amen.

Hail health of the world, Word of the father, true sacred host, truly living flesh, wholly God, truly man: Body of our Lord Jesus Christ who created me, be merciful to me. Amen.

Comment.   Sacramental prayer.

8. *Ave virginum gemma Catharina*

Ave virginum gemma Catharina. Ave sponsa regis regum gloriosa. Ave viva Christi hostia. Tua venerantibus patrocinia impetrata non deneges suffragia. Amen.

Hail precious virgin Catherine. Hail glorious bride of the King of Kings. Hail living host of Christ. Through the gift of your adoring protection, do not deny judgment. Amen.

Comment.   Magnificat antiphon, Feast of St. Catherine.

9. *Benedicimus te*

Benedicimus te, clementissime Deus, qui diem festum beati Anthonii in laudem tuam nobis expendere tribuisti. Teque suppliciter exoramus ut sanctis tuis quibus honorificentiam exhibemus virtute ac premio sociari mereamur.

We bless you, most merciful God, who allowed us to sing your praises on the day of the feast of blessed Anthony. And we most humbly pray to you that we will be worthy to be united with your saints, to whom we show honor, by virtue and favor.

Comment.   Unidentified text, Feast of St. Anthony.

10–13. *Domine salvum fac regem*

Domine salvum fac regem: et exaudi nos in die qua invocaverimus te.

O Lord save the king: and mercifully hear us when we call upon you.

Comment.   Psalm 19:10.

14. *Duo seraphim*

Duo seraphim clamabant alter ad alterum:
   Sanctus, Sanctus, Sanctus Dominus Deus Sabaoth. Plena est omnis terra gloria ejus.
   Tres sunt qui testimonium dant in caelo: Pater, Verbum, et Spiritus Sanctus: et hi tres unum sunt.

Two seraphim cried to one another:
   "Holy, Holy, Holy Lord God of Sabaoth. Heaven and earth are full of your glory."
   Three are they who bear witness in heaven: Father, Word, and Holy Spirit: and these three are one.

Comment.   Responsory, Feast of the Trinity.

15. *Ecce panis Angelorum*

Ecce panis Angelorum,	Behold the bread of Angels,
Factus cibus viatorum:	made the food of travelers:
Vere panis filiorum,	the true bread of children,
Non mittendus canibus.	not to be given to dogs.

Comment.   Verse 21, Lauda Sion, sequence for Corpus Christi.

16. *Fons aquae vivae*

Fons aquae vivae emanavit super nos, alleluja:
Et sicut flores paradisi rigavit nos, alleluja.

Ut in amore Jesu florescant animae sanctorum,
Et lilia Virginum suavitatis odoris infundant.
O Jesu fons amoris, infunde roram gratiarum,
Et in odorem unguentorum ibimus,
Et laetantis cantabimus, alleluja.

The spring of living water has flowed over us, alleluia:
And just as it has watered the flowers of paradise, it has watered us, alleluia.

As the souls of the blessed blossom in the love of Jesus,
and lilies of the virgins pour out sweet odor.
O Jesus, spring of love, pour out your grace,
and we shall walk into the fragrance of ointment
and sing joyfully, alleluia.

Comment. Unidentified baptismal text.

17. *Hic est beatissimus*

Hic est beatissimus Evangelista et Apostolus Joannes. Cum privilegio amoris praecipui caeteris altius a Domino meruisti honorari. Hic est discipulus ille quem diligebat Jesus qui super pectus Domini in caena recubuit.

This is the most blessed Evangelist and Apostle John. With the privilege of a love from God higher than the rest, you deserve honor. This is the disciple whom Jesus loved, who, at the last supper, reclined on the breast of the Lord.

Comment. Responsory, Feast of St. John the Evangelist.

18. *O athletum invictissimum*

O athletum invictissimum episcopum Gatianum qui gloriosam triumphi sui coronam percepturus vidit, sibi a Domino dare viaticum, audire meruit, ne metuas, quia ad patriam caelestum te transferam quo laureatus exultes. Amen.

O unconquered champion, Bishop Gatianus, who saw in a vision the glorious crown of his triumph, himself being given viaticum by the Lord, you deserve to hear [these words]: "Do not be afraid, for I will carry you, who exults the crowned one, to the heavenly dwelling place." Amen.

Comment. Unidentified text, Feast of St. Gatien.

19. *O crux ave*

O crux ave, spes unica,
Hoc passionis tempore
Auge piis justitiam,
Reisque dona veniam.

Hail, O cross, one hope,
at this passion time
give justice to the faithful,
and mercy to those awaiting judgement.

Comment. Verse 6, "Vexilla Regis," hymn for Passion Sunday.

20. *O Doctor optime*

O Doctor optime, Ecclesiae sanctae lumen, beate Augustine, divinae legis amator: deprecare pro nobis Filium Dei. Amen.

O most perfect Teacher, light of the holy church, blessed Augustine, lover of divine law: pray for us to the Son of God. Amen.

Comment. Magnificat antiphon, Feast of St. Augustine.

21. *O Pastor aeterne*

O Pastor aeterne, o clemens et bone custos, qui dum devoti gregis preces attendere, voce lapsa de caelo praesuli sanctissimo, dignum Episcopatum Nicolaum, ostendisti tantum famulum. Amen.

O eternal shepherd, O merciful and good guardian, while your flock was intent on prayer, you in a voice from heaven revealed to the most solemn of the leader so great a servant as Nicolas worthy to be bishop.

Comment. Magnificat antiphon, Feast of St. Nicolas.

22. *O quam suavis*

O quam suavis es, Domine, spiritus tuus! qui ut dulcedinem tuam in filios demonstrares nos cibo tuo replesti suavissimo. O bone Jesu, salvum fac sponsam tuam, conserva populum tuum, et da nobis pacem, et vitam aeternam. Amen.

O how sweet, Lord, is your spirit! Who, that you might show your sweetness to your sons, have filled us with the sweetest meal. O good Jesus, make safe your bride, preserve your people, and give us peace, and eternal life. Amen.

Comment. Magnificat antiphon, Feast of Corpus Christi.

23. *O sacrum convivium*

O sacrum convivium, in quo Christus sumitur: recolitur memoria passionis ejus: mens impletur gratia: et futurae gloriae nobis pignus datur. Alleluja.

O sacred banquet, in which Christ is received: the memory of his passion is renewed: the mind is filled with grace: and a promise of glory to come is given to us. Alleluia.

Comment. Sacramental prayer.

24. *Popule meus*

Popule meus, quid feci tibi? aut in quo contristavi te? responde mihi.
Quia eduxi te de terra Aegypti: parasti crucem Salvatori tuo.
Propter te flagellavi Aegyptum: et tu me flagellatum tradidisti.

My people, what have I done to you? Or in what have I troubled you? Answer me.
Because I led you out of the land of Egypt: you prepared a cross for your Savior.
Because of you I scourged Egypt: and you handed me over to be scourged.

Comment. Based on text to Improperia, Good Friday.

25. *Pretiosus Domini Dionysius*

Pretiosus Domini Dionysius in agone novissimo dixit: nunc jam Domine per coronam martyrii cum fratribus meis servis tuis suscipe me. Tuosque Domine mi tuae custodiae commendo quos ministerio nostro et tibi tuo sanguine acquisisti. Cunctos qui te per nos in nomine tuo petierint ut pollicitus et clementer exaudi.

The Lord's precious Dionysius, in utmost agony cried: now, Lord, by the crown of the martyrs, with my brothers who are your servants, accept me. My Lord, I commend your servants, whom you have gained by our ministry and your blood, into your safe-keeping. Mercifully hear all those who through us in your name entreat you as promised.

Comment. Responsory, Feast of Saint Denis.

26–28. *Regina caeli*

Regina caeli laetare, alleluja:
Quia quem meruisti portare, alleluja:
Resurrexit, sicut dixit, alleluja:
Ora pro nobis, Deum, alleluja.

Queen of heaven, rejoice, alleluia:
For he whom you deserved to bear, alleluia:
Has risen, as he said, alleluia:
Pray for us to God, alleluia.

Comment. Marian antiphon.

29. *Regnum mundi*

Regnum mundi et omnem ornatum saeculi contempsi, propter amorem Domini mei, Jesu Christi. Quem vidi, quem amavi, in quem credidi, quem dilexi, alleluja.

Eructavit cor meum verbum bonum, dico ego opera mea regi.
Gloria Patri, et Filio, et Spiritui Sancto.

I had contempt for the kingdom of this world and all secular things, because of the love of my Lord, Jesus Christ. Whom I saw, whom I loved, in whom I believed, in whom I have delighted, alleluia.

My heart overflows with a good word. I address my work to the king.
Glory to the Father, and the Son, and the Holy Spirit.

Comment. Responsory, Ceremony of the Vesture of Novices.

30–32. *Salve Regina*

Salve Regina, mater misericordiae: Vita, dulcedo, et spes nostra, salve. Ad te clamamus, exsules, filii Evae. Ad te suspiramus, gementes et flentes in hac lacrimarum valle. Eja ergo, Advocata nostra, illos tuos misericordes oculos ad nos converte. Et Jesum, benedictum fructum ventris tui, nobis post hoc exsilium ostende. O clemens: O pia: O dulcis Virgo Maria.

Hail Queen, mother of mercy: our life, sweetness, and hope, hail. To you we cry, exiled children of Eve. To you we sigh, mourning and weeping in this vale of tears. Come then, our advocate, turn your merciful eyes to us. And after this exile, show to us the blessed fruit of your womb, Jesus. O clement: O pious: O sweet Virgin Mary.

Comment. Marian antiphon.

33. Sancta Maria

Sancta Maria, succurre miseris, juva pusillanimes, refove flebiles: ora pro populo, interveni pro clero, intercede pro devoto femineo sexu: sentiant omnes tuum juvamen, quicumque celebrant tuam sanctam commemorationem. Alleluja.

Holy Mary, aid the helpless, strengthen the weak, comfort the sorrowful: pray for the people, plead for the clergy, intercede for all holy women: let all who celebrate your holy commemoration be aware of your strength. Alleluia.

Comment. Magnificat antiphon, Feast of Notre Dame des Neiges.

34. Tu es Petrus

Tu es Petrus, et super hanc petram aedificabo Ecclesiam meam: et portas inferni non praevalebunt adversus eam. Amen.

You are Peter, and on this rock I will build my Church: and the gates of hell will not prevail against it. Amen.

Comment. Offertory, Feast of Saint Peter.

35. Tu es vas electionis

Tu es vas electionis, Sancte Paule Apostole, praedicator veritatis et doctor gentium, per quem omnes gentes cognoverunt gratiam Dei. Intercede pro nobis ad Deum qui te elegit. Alleluja.

You are the chosen vessel, Saint Paul the Apostle, preacher of truth and teacher of the people, by whom all Gentiles will come to know the love of God. Pray for us to God who chose you. Alleluia.

Comment. Antiphon, Feast of Saint Paul.

36. Veni Sancte Spiritus

Veni Sancte Spiritus, reple tuorum corda fidelium: et tui amoris in eis ignem accende. Qui per diversitatem cunctarum linguarum gentes in unitate fidei congregasti. Alleluja.

Come Holy Spirit, fill the hearts of your faithful: and ignite in them the fire of your love. You, through the diversity of all languages, have joined all peoples in unity of faith. Alleluia.

Comment. Antiphon, Feast of Pentecost.

37. Vir Domini Benedictus

Vir Domini Benedictus omnium justorum spiritu plenus fuit: ipse intercedat pro cunctis monasticae professionis. Alleluja.

Benedict, man of God, was made full by the spirits of all the just: he himself interceded for the profession of all monastics. Alleluia.

Comment. Unidentifed text, Ceremony of Profession.

Hymns

38. Ad caenam Agni

Ad caenam Agni providi,
Et stolis albis candidi,
Post transitum maris rubri,
Christo canamus principi.

At the prescient Lamb's feast,
and dressed in white robes,
after crossing the Red Sea,
we sing praises to Christ our prince.

Cujus corpus sanctissimum,
In ara crucis torridum,
Cruore ejus roseo
Gustando vivimus Deo.

Whose most holy body,
hung parched on the altar of the cross,
by tasting his blood
we live in God.

Protecti Paschae vespero
A devastante Angelo,
Erepti de durissimo
Pharaonis imperio.

Protected on Passover's eve
from the devastating Angel,
spared from the ruthless
command of the Pharaoh.

Jam Pascha nostrum Christus est,
Qui immolatus Agnus est,
Sinceritatis azyma,
Caro ejus oblata est.

Now Christ is our paschal sacrifice,
the Lamb sacrificed for us,
the unleavened bread of sincerity,
his flesh is offered.

O vere digna hostia, Per quam fracta sunt tartara, Redempta plebs captivita, Reddita vitae praemia.	O true and worthy host, by whom hell is destroyed, the captives set free, and eternal life restored.
Consurgit Christus tumulo, Victor redit de barathro, Tyrannum trudens vinculo, Et Paradisum reserans.	Christ rises from the grave, he is victorious over the abyss, chaining the tyrant and regaining paradise.
Quaesumus, Auctor omnium, In hoc paschali gaudio, Ab omni mortis impetu Tuum defende populum.	We pray, O author of all, in this paschal celebration, defend your people from all mortal dangers.
Gloria tibi Domine, Qui surrexisti a mortuis, Cum Patre et Sancto Spiritu, In sempiterna saecula.	Glory to you Lord, who rose from the dead, with the Father and the Holy Spirit, now and for ever. Amen.

Comment. Easter hymn.

39. Alleluja. O filii et filiae

Alleluja, alleluja.	Alleluia, alleluia.
O filii et filiae, Rex caelestis, Rex gloriae, Morte surrexit hodie. Alleluja.	O sons and daughters, the King of heaven, the King of glory, has today defeated death. Alleluia.
Et mane prima sabathi, Ad ostium monumenti, Accesserunt discipuli. Alleluja.	And on that first sabbath morning, the disciples approached the door of the tomb. Alleluia.
Vide, Thoma, vide latus, Vide pedes, vide manus, Noli esse incredulus. Alleluja.	See, Thomas, see his side, see his feet, see his hands, do not be doubtful. Alleluia.

Comment. Easter hymn.

40. Aurea luce

Aurea luce et decore roseo, Lux lucis omne perfudisti saeculum, Decorans caelos inclito martyrio, Hac sacra die, quae dat reis veniam.	With golden light and rose-colored honor, light of light, you bathed the world, adorning the skies with celebrated martyrdom, on this holy day, which gives pardon to the guilty ones.
Janitor caeli, Doctor orbis pariter, Judices saecli, vera mundi lumina: Per crucem alter, alter ense triumphans, Vitae senatum laureati possident.	Gatekeeper of heaven, and teacher of the earth likewise, judges of the generations, true lights of the world: one triumphant by the cross, the other by the sword, crowned in laurel, they will sit in the senate of life.
O felix Roma quae tantorum principum, Es purpurata pretiosa sanguine, Non laude tua sed ipsorum meritis, Excellis omnem mundi pulchritudinem.	O happy Rome, stained purple with the precious blood of so many princes, not by your own glory but by their merits you excel all the beauty of the world.

Comment. Feast of St. Peter and St. Paul.

41. Ave maris stella

Ave maris stella, Dei Mater alma,	Hail, star of the sea, caring Mother of God,

Atque semper Virgo,	and forever Virgin,
Felix caeli porta.	happy gate of heaven.
Sumens illud Ave	Receiving that Ave
Gabrielis ore,	from the mouth of Gabriel,
Funda nos in pace,	establish us in peace,
Mutans Evae nomen.	transforming the name of Eve.
Solve vincla reis,	Loosen the chains of the guilty,
Profer lumen caecis:	bring light to the blind:
Mala nostra pelle,	drive out our evil,
Bona cuncta posce.	ask all good things for us.
Monstra te esse matrem:	Show yourself to be a mother:
Sumat per te preces,	through you may he receive prayers,
Qui pro nobis natus,	who, born for us,
Tulit esse tuus.	suffered to be yours.
Virgo singularis,	Singular Virgin,
Inter omnes mitis,	gentle amongst all others,
Nos culpis solutos,	make us free from our sins,
Mites fac et castos.	gentle and chaste.
Vitam praesta puram,	Keep life pure,
Iter para tutum:	make the journey safe:
Ut videntes Jesum,	so that seeing Jesus,
Semper collaetemur.	we may always rejoice.
Sit laus Deo Patri,	Praise to God the Father
Summo Christo decus,	and to the most glorious Christ,
Spiritui Sancto,	and to the Holy Spirit,
Tribus honor unus. Amen.	one honor to the three. Amen.

Comment. Marian hymn.

42. *Ave mater pia*

Ave mater pia,	Hail faithful mother,
Ex qua nobis orta	from whom is descended
Est Virgo Maria,	the Virgin Mary,
Felix caeli porta.	happy gate of heaven.
Sumens sacrum fetum	Receiving the holy child
Ad salutem omen	as a sign,
Nostrum delens fletum,	staunching our cries,
Mutans Evae nomen.	transforming the name of Eve.
Solve vincla nexis,	Loosen the chains of the bound,
Preces nostras nosce,	receive our prayers,
Sordes lava fessis,	cleanse the stains of the weary,
Bona cuncta posce.	ask all good things for us.
Monstra, quod sis mater	Show us that you are the mother
Matris, per quam suus	of the mother, through whom
Filius et pater	you brought into being
Tulis esse tuus.	her son and father.
Virgo, matris prece	Virgin, by the mother's prayer
Panes vitae pastos,	make the breads of life nourishing,
Facias nos faece	purify us from the
Carnis dempta castos.	discarded dregs of flesh.
Vitam nostram munda,	Make our life pure
Ut sic gloriemur	that we might live in glory,
Et luce jucunda	and that in your sweet light
Semper collaetemur.	we will always rejoice.

Sit laus et honoris	Let there be praise and the service of honor
Soli Deo munus,	to God alone,
Nunc et cunctis horis	now and for ever
Tribus honor unus. Amen.	honor the three in one.

    Comment.   Feast of St. Anne.

43. *Christe redemptor omnium, Conserva*

Christe redemptor omnium,	Christ, redeemer of all,
Conserva tuos famulos,	save your servants,
Beatae semper Virginis	reconciled by the holy prayers
Placatus sanctis precibus.	of the Virgin.
Beata quoque agmina	Blessed procession of
Caelestium spirituum,	heavenly spirits,
Praeterita, praesentia,	protect us from past, present,
Futura mala pellite.	and future evil.
Vates aeterni Judicis,	To the prophets of the eternal Judge
Apostolique Domini,	and apostles of the Lord,
Suppliciter exposcimus	we humbly beg
Salvari vestris precibus.	to be saved by your prayers.
Martyres Dei inclyti,	Glorious martyrs of God,
Confessoresque lucidi,	and shining confessors,
Vestris orationibus	through your prayers
Nos ferte in caelestibus.	lift us up to heaven.
Chori sanctarum Virginum,	Choirs of holy virgins,
Monachorumque omnium,	and of all monks,
Simul cum Sanctis omnibus	with all the saints
Consortes Christi facite.	make a consort for Christ!
Gentem auferte perfidam	Expel the faithless tribe
Credentium de finibus	from the borders of the believing
Ut Christo laudes debitas	so that we might eagerly give
Persolvamus alacriter.	the praises we owe to Christ.
Gloria Patri ingenito,	Glory to the one-born God,
Ejusque Unigenito,	and to his only begotten Son,
Una cum Sancto Spiritu,	one with the Holy Spirit,
In sempiterna saecula. Amen.	for ever and ever. Amen.

    Comment.   Feast of All Saints.

44. *Christe redemptor omnium, Ex Patre*

Christe redemptor omnium,	Christ, redeemer of all,
Ex Patre, Patris unice,	from the Father, the Father's only [son],
Solus ante principium	alone before the world began,
Natus ineffabiliter.	born ineffable.
Tu lumen, tu splendor Patris,	You light, you splendor of the Father,
Tu spes perennis omnium:	you eternal hope of all:
Intende quos fundunt preces	accept the prayers that your servants
Tui per orbem famuli.	pour out throughout the world.
Memento salutis Auctor,	Remember, agent of salvation,
Quod nostri quondam corporis,	that at one time you assumed
Ex illibata Virgine	our corporal form,
Nascendo, formam sumpseris.	through birth from a spotless virgin.
Hic praesens testatur dies,	Thus testifies the present day
Currens per anni circulum,	through the cycle of the years,
Quod solus a sede Patris	that you alone have come from the Father's throne
Mundi salus adveneris.	as savior of the world.

Hunc caelum, terra, hunc mare,	This sky, earth, this sea
Hunc omne quod in eis est,	and all that is in it,
Auctorem adventus tui	are exalted in song by the one
Laudans exsultat cantico.	who praises the agent of your coming.
Nos quoque, qui sancto tuo	And we, who by your precious blood
Redempti sanguine sumus,	are redeemed
Ob diem natalis tui	on the day of your birth,
Hymnum novum concinimus.	sing a new hymn.
Gloria tibi Domine,	Glory to you Lord,
Qui natus est de Virgine,	who was born of the Virgin,
Cum Patre et Sancto Spiritu,	with the Father and the Holy Spirit,
In sempiterna saecula.	for ever and ever.

Comment. Feast of the Nativity.

45. Claris conjubila

Claris conjubila Gallia laudibus,	Famous Gaul, rejoice in praises,
Laeteris Benedicti Patris ossibus,	celebrate the relics of Benedict the father
Felixque gremio condita patria,	and, happily restored to its homeland from the depths,
Servas membra celebria.	protect the honored limbs.
Miris Italia fulserat actibus.	Italy gleamed in miraculous feats.
Gallos irradiat corpore mortuus;	The deceased illuminates the Gauls with his body;
Signis ad tumulum crebrius emicat,	he breaks forth from his grave with signs frequently,
Illustrans patriam novam.	lighting up his new homeland.
Hic vatum veterum facta resuscitat,	This one revives the deeds of the ancient prophets,
Morti, quod libuit, mortuus imperat;	the deceased commands death as he pleases.
Extinctum proprius ossibus excitat:	With his bones he brings back to life one who passed away:
O quam mira potentia.	O such a miraculous power.
Jam caelo residens, o Pater optime,	Now residing in heaven, O great Father,
Divinis famulos imbue regulis,	instruct your servants in the divine rules,
Angustum per iter scandere largius	by which to climb the narrow path,
Dona regna perennia.	give sovereignty for ever.
Cunctorum dominans omnipotentia,	You who with supreme power rule all you see
Quae de sede poli conspicis omnia:	from the seat of heaven:
Psallentum placide suscipe cantica,	receive the singer's hymns peacefully,
Votis, voce precantia. Amen.	which supplicate with heart and voice. Amen.

Comment. Feast of the Translation of St. Benedict.

46. Dionysii martyris

Dionysii martyris	Of the merits of Dionysius the martyr
Et sociorum merita,	and his companions,
Cum clero cantat celebris	with the clergy, the famous
Conventus in Ecclesia.	convent sings in the church.
Ad Gallos missi principes,	Sent to the Gauls as the first,
Caelestis lumen gloriae	the three leaders bring
Per gradus Archipraesides	the light of heavenly glory
Spargebant tres Lutetiae.	to the doorsteps of Paris.
Ab idolorum revocant	They turn the hearts
Cultu corda gentilium,	from the worship of pagan idols,
Arasque Louis dissipant,	and they demolish the altars of Louis,
Prosternunt et Mercurium.	and they cast down Mercury.
Sed ne repente crederet	But so that not the entire nation
Gens tota Dionysio	believes the rash Dionysius
Et Clementis se subderet	and submits to
Romani Pontificio,	the pontificate of Clement the Roman,

Tiranni diram rabiem	the malice of the faithless tyrant
Livor accendit impii	brings forth a dreadful fury,
Demon auget saevitiam	and a demon increases the vengefulness of
Praefecti tum Fescennii.	Fescennius, the prefect at the time.

Saevit per ignem, per cruces,
Et per ardorem clibani,
Per rotas, et feras truces;
Sanctis sed crescunt animi.

It rages through fire, through crucifixion,
and through the heat of the furnace,
through wheels and fierce wild animals:
but the spirits of the saints grow.

Hinc furor, hinc benevoli
Truncatur caput Martyris
Galliarum Apostoli,
Duobus simul sociis.

In this fury, now
the head of the kind martyr,
apostle to the Gauls, is cut off,
at the same time as those of his two companions.

Caeli gaudet exercitus,
Corpus circumdat Praesulis
Dum caput gestat manibus
Sacris et ludit canticis.

The heavenly army rejoices,
it surrounds the body of the prelate
while he carries his head in his hands
and celebrates with sacred songs.

Illos ter Sancta Trinitas
Coronis ornat gloriae,
Post cruces et angustias
Triumpham dat victoriae.

The thrice holy Trinity
adorns them with crowns of glory,
and after the crosses and sufferings
grants them the triumph of victory.

Fusa plebs in itinere
Passim subit Martyrium,
Per vicos caepit fluere
Sanguis caesorum corporum.

Unrestrained pilgrims from all places
approach the site of martyrdom;
the blood of the slaughtered bodies
begins to flow through the streets.

Invicta fides Martyrum
Per innocentem sanguinem
Tirannum vincit perfidum,
Prosternit mundi principem.

By innocent blood,
the invincible faith of the martyrs
conquers the faithless tyrant,
and overthrows worldly authority.

Te summa Deus Trinitas
Tres nunc Gallorum ordines
Precamur semper foveas
Hos per tres Archi-Martires.

We pray that you, God and highest Trinity,
show favor
to the three estates of France
through these three arch-martyrs.

Fidem professos aspice
Forti redemptos brachio
Dionysio auspice
Da frui caeli gaudia. Amen.

Behold those who professed faith
redeemed by the strong arm,
and, under the protection of Dionysius,
grant us to enjoy the delights of heaven. Amen.

Comment.   From Jacques Doublet, *Histoire chronologique pour la verité de S. Denys Areopagite apostre de France et premier evesque de Paris* (Paris: Pierre de Bresche, 1646), 487–88.

47. Iste Confessor

Iste Confessor Domini sacratus,
Festa plebs cujus celebrat per orbem,
Hodie laetus meruit secreta
Scandere caeli.

That sacred confessor of the Lord,
whose feast all celebrate throughout the world,
today joyfully deserves
to ascend to the mysteries of heaven.

Qui pius, prudens, humilis, pudicus,
Sobrius, castus fuit et quietus,
Vita dum praesens, vegetavit ejus
Corporis artus.

Who was pious, prudent, humble, virtuous,
sober, chaste, and quiet,
as long as he lived,
his body was strong.

Cujus ob praestans meritum frequenter,
Aegra quae passim jacuere membra,
Viribus morbi domitis, saluti
Restituuntur.

Because of his outstanding merits,
his broken limbs, which lay spread out,
were restored to health
after the taming of the forces of sickness.

Noster hinc illi chorus obsequentum
Concinit laudem celebresque palmas,
Ut piis ejus precibus juvemur
Omne per aevum.

Sit salus illi, decus, atque virtus,
Qui super caeli solio coruscans,
Totius mundi seriem gubernat,
Trinus et unus. Amen.

Henceforth our obedient chorus
sings to him praise and glorious hymns,
so that we may help his faithful with prayers,
throughout all ages.

Let there be prosperity, glory, and virtue,
to him whose throne rushes over the heavens,
and governs the whole world in turn,
three in one. Amen.

Comment. Common of Confessors.

48. *Jesu, nostra redemptio*

Jesu, nostra redemptio,
Amor et desiderium,
Deus Creator omnium,
Homo in fine temporum.

Quae te vicit clementia,
Ut ferres nostra crimina,
Crudelem mortem patiens,
Ut nos a morte tolleres!

Inferni claustra penetrans,
Tuos capitivos redimens,
Victor triumpho nobili
Ad dextram Patris residens:

Ipsa te cogat pietas,
Ut mala nostra superes
Parcendo, et voti compotes
Nos tuo vultu saties.

Tu esto nostrum gaudium,
Qui es futurus praemium:
Sit nostra in te Gloria
Per cuncta semper saecula. Amen.

Jesus, our redemption,
love and desire,
God Creator of all,
man at the end of time.

What clemency has overcome you
who bears our sins
suffering a cruel death
to spare us from death!

Breaking the bonds of hell,
redeeming your captives,
victorious in noble triumph,
seated at the right hand of the Father.

May piety herself summon you,
that you might redeem our sins,
and with vows fulfilled
may you satiate us with your countenance.

Be our joy,
you who are our reward to come:
let us be in your Glory
for all ages. Amen.

Comment. Feast of the Ascension.

49. *O gloriosae virgines*

O gloriosae virgines,
Cum angelis jam divites,
Sponsa tenetis Dominum,
Caelum cubile sanctum.

Quod gessistis jam habetis,
Nobis adeste miseris,
Ut nos absolvat Dominus,
Per vos cunctis criminibus. Alleluja.

O glorious virgins,
with the angels you are rich now,
as a bride you hold the Lord,
heaven is your holy bed.

That which you carried, now you hold,
be near us sinners,
that God might absolve us
of our crimes through you. Alleluia.

Comment. Unidentified hymn, Common of Virgins.

50. *O salutaris hostia*

O salutaris hostia,
Quae caeli pandis ostium:
Bella premunt hostilia,
Da robur, fer auxilium.

O saving host,
who opens the door to heaven:
hostile wars oppress us,
give strength, bear aid.

Comment. Final verse of "Verbum supernum prodiens," hymn for the Benediction of Blessed Sacrament, Feast of Corpus Christi.

51. Pange lingua . . . Corporis

Pange lingua gloriosi
Corporis mysterium,
Sanguinisque pretiosi,
Quem in mundi pretium
Fructus ventris generosi
Rex effudit gentium.

Nobis datus, nobis natus,
Ex intacta Virgine,
Et in mundo conversatus,
Sparso verbi semine,
Sui moras incolatus
Miro clausit ordine. Amen.

Sing, my tongue, the glory
of the mystery of flesh,
and of the precious blood,
which for the world,
fruit of a noble womb,
the King shed.

Given to us, born for us,
from a pure Virgin,
and dwelling in the world,
sowing the seeds of truth,
his life of woe
he wondrously concluded. Amen.

   Comment. Feast of Corpus Christi.

52. Pange lingua . . . Certaminis

Pange lingua gloriosi
Virginem certaminis,
Martyrumque ter beata
Luce palmas nobiles:
Quas sacrarum victimarum
Sanguis Agno funditur.

Ursullae prudens propago,
Digna caelo conscio
Chrisma pleno vale gestans
Et paratas lampades
Nuptiis dignata sponsi
Se sacris miscet choris. Amen.

Sing, my tongue, the glory
of the battle, virgin
and martyr three times blessed,
shine noble victor:
for this holy victim
the Lamb's blood is shed.

Ursula's wise offspring,
worthy to know heaven,
bearing unction
and prepared lamps,
worthy to marry the bridegroom
mingles with the heavenly chorus. Amen.

   Comment. Feast of St. Ursula.

53. Quam pulchra es

Quam pulchra es amica mea.

O gloriosa domina
Excelsa super sidera:
Qui te creavit, provide,
Lactasti sacro ubere.

Quod Eva tristis abstulit,
Tu reddis almo germine:
Intrent ut astra flebiles,
Caeli fenestra facta es.

How beautiful you are, my friend.

O glorious mistress,
exalted above the stars:
him who created you,
you fed with your sacred breast.

That which the sorrowful Eve withdrew,
your sacred womb restores:
so that the tearful may reach the stars
you become a window to heaven.

   Comment. Second half of "Quem terra, pontus," hymn for Lauds, Common of the Blessed Virgin Mary.

54. Veni Creator Spiritus

Veni Creator Spiritus,
Mentes tuorum visita:
Imple superna gratia
Quae tu creasti pectora.

Qui diceris Paraclitus,
Altissimi donum Dei,
Fons vivus, ignis, caritas,
Et spiritalis unctio.

Come Creator Spirit,
visit the souls of your people:
fill with your supernal grace
the hearts which you created.

You who are called Paraclete,
gift of God most high,
fountain of life, fire, love,
and spiritual unction.

Tu septiformis munere, Dextrae Dei tu digitus, Tu rite promissum Patris, Sermone ditans guttura.	You sevenfold offering, you finger of God's right hand, you promise of the Father, enriching throats with speech.
Accende lumen sensibus, Infunde amorem cordibus, Infirma nostri corporis, Virtute firmas perpeti.	Kindle light in our senses, fill our hearts with love, you make the weakness of our body strong by your perpetual virtue.
Hostem repellas longius, Pacemque dones protinus: Ductore sic te praevio, Vitemus omne noxium.	You drive our enemy far away, and give us peace now: so with you as guide ahead we shall avoid all danger.
Per te sciamus da Patrem, Noscamus atque Filium, Teque utriusque Spiritum Credamus omni tempore.	Through you we know the Father, and we recognize the Son, and we believe in you, the Spirit of both, for all time.
Gloria Patri Domino, Natoque qui a mortuis, Surrexit, ac Paraclito, In saeculorum saecula. Amen.	Glory to God the Father and to the Son, who rose from the dead, and to the Paraclete, forever. Amen.

Comment. Feast of Pentecost.

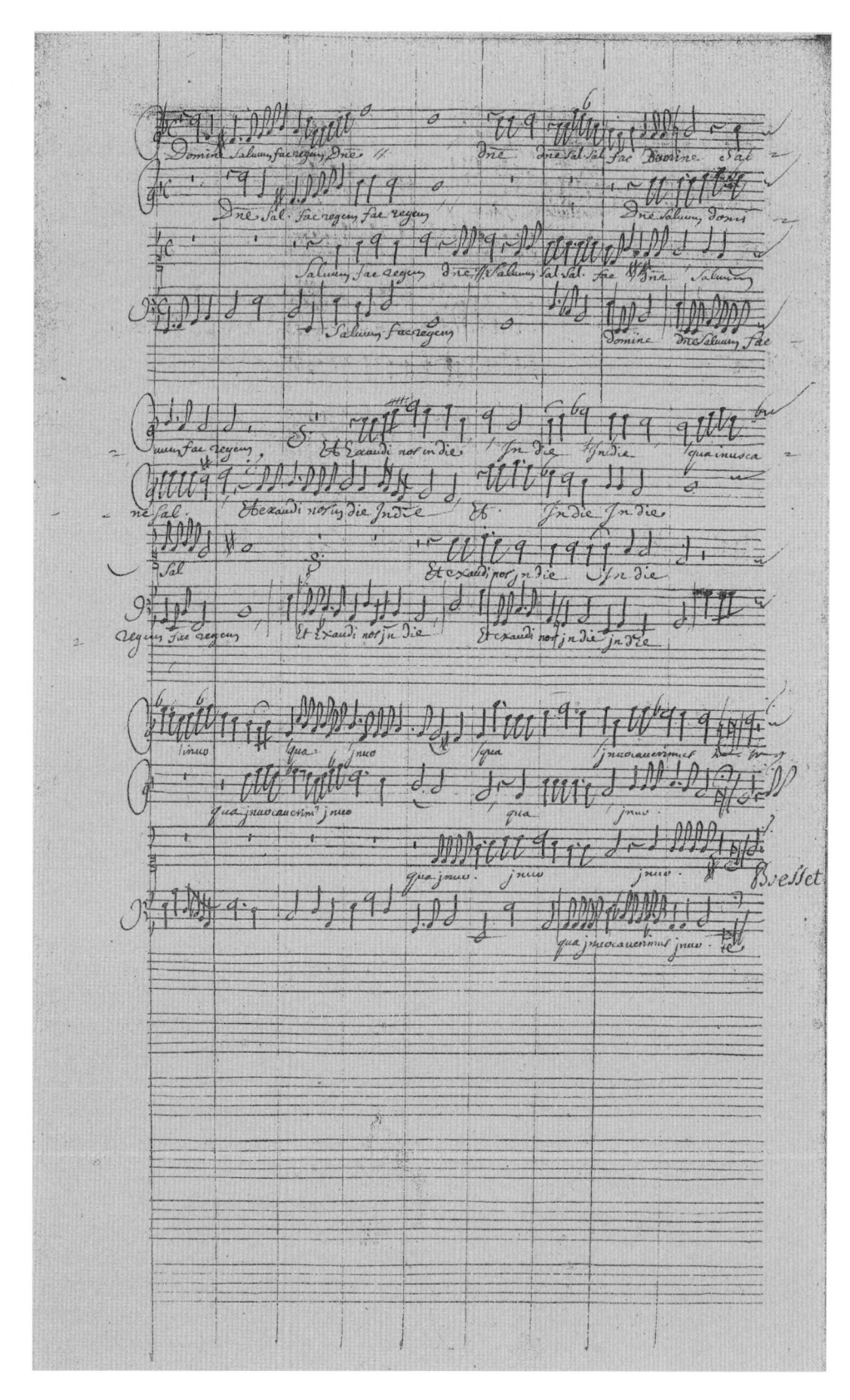

Plate 1. Antoine Boesset, "Domine salvum fac regem (2)" with attribution to "Boesset." Paris, Bibliothèque nationale de France, Département de la Musique, Rés. V^(ma) ms. 571, folio 1v. Reproduced with permission from the Bibliothèque nationale de France.

Plate 2. Antoine Boesset, Magnificat (1), measures 1–18, with bass line sketches and psalm tone concordant with the *Antiphonier... de Montmartre*. Paris, Bibliothèque nationale de France, Département de la Musique, Rés. V^ma ms. 571, folio 155v. Reproduced with permission from the Bibliothèque nationale de France.

Plate 3. *Antiphonier Bénédictin pour les réligieuses du Royal et célèbre monastère de Montmartre* (Paris: L. Sevestre, 1646), page 520, showing Magnificat tone concordant with Rés. 571. Paris, Bibliothèque nationale de France. Reproduced with permission from the Bibliothèque nationale de France.

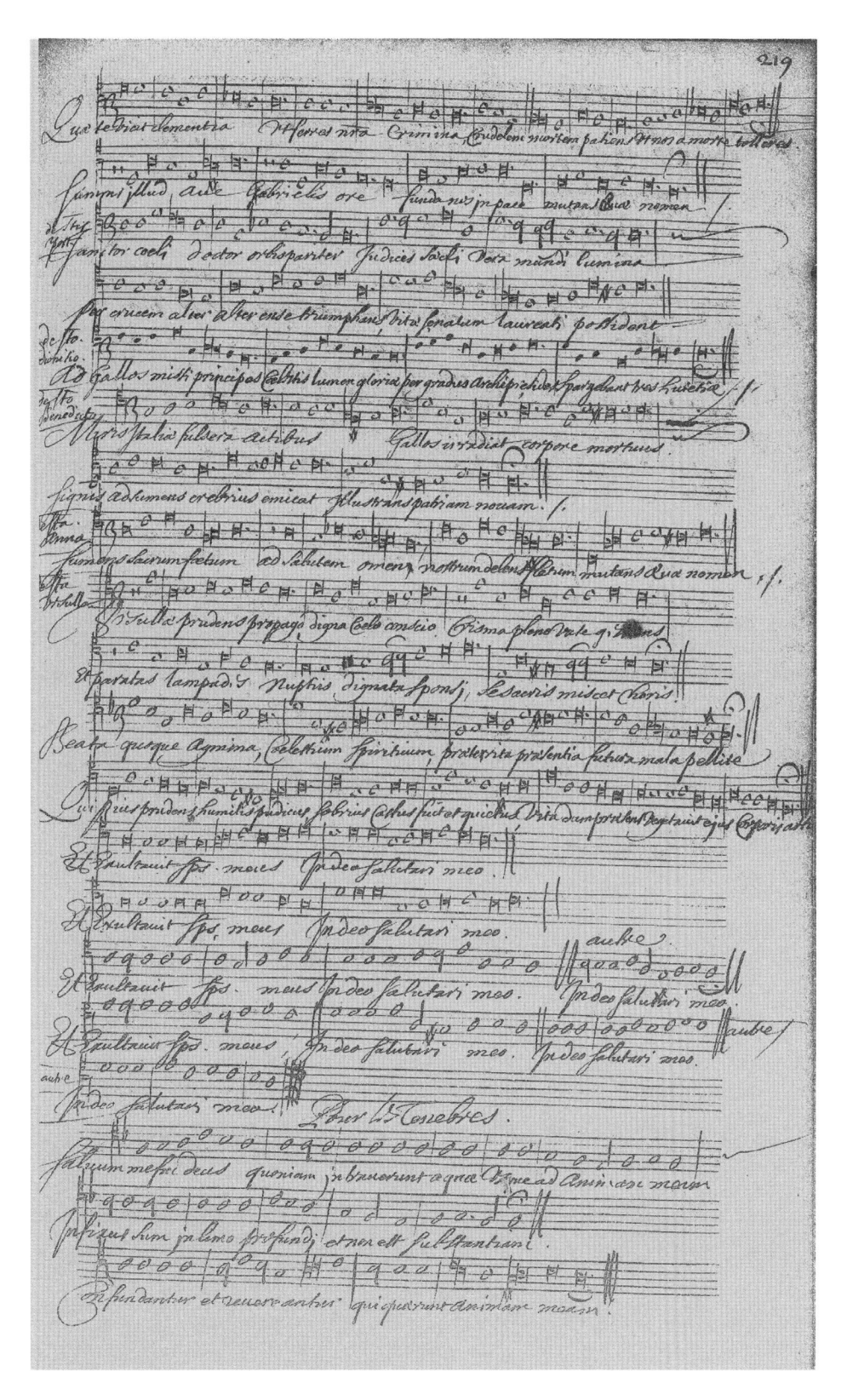

Plate 4. Rhythmicized versions of hymn melodies, Magnificat tones, and Tenebrae tones. Paris, Bibliothèque nationale de France, Département de la Musique, Rés. V^{ma} ms. 571, folio 219r. Reproduced with permission from the Bibliothèque nationale de France.

Motets

1. Alma Redemptoris Mater

16
-re, suc- cur- re ca- den- ti sur- ge- re qui cu- rat po- pu- lo, sur- ge- re qui
sur- ge- re qui cu- rat po- pu- lo, sur- ge- re qui
sur- ge- re qui cu- rat po- pu- lo, sur- ge- re qui
sur- ge- re qui cu- rat po- pu- lo, sur- ge- re qui
20
cu- rat po- pu- lo: quae ge- nu- i- sti, na-
cu- rat po- pu- lo: Tu quae ge- nu- i- sti, quae ge- nu- i- - sti, na-
cu- rat po- pu- lo: quae ge- nu- i- - sti, na-
cu- rat po- pu- lo: quae ge- nu- i- sti, na-
26
-tu- ra mi-ran- te, tu- um san- ctum Ge- ni- to- rem, san- - ctum Ge- ni-
-tu- ra mi- ran- te, tu- um san- ctum Ge- ni- to- rem, san- - ctum Ge- ni-
-tu- ra mi- ran- te, tu- um san- ctum Ge- ni- to- rem,
-tu- ra mi- ran- te, tu- um san- ctum Ge- ni- to- rem,

31
-to- rem, san- ctum, san- ctum Ge- ni- to- rem: Vir- - go pri-
- to- rem, san- - ctum Ge- ni- to- rem:
san- ctum Ge- ni- to- rem:
san- - ctum Ge- ni- to- rem:
36
-us ac po- ste- ri- us, Vir- go pri- us ac po- ste- ri- us, Ga- bri- e-
Vir- go pri- us ac po- ste- ri- us, Ga- bri- e-
Vir- go pri- us ac po- ste- ri- us, Ga- bri- e-
Vir- go pri- us ac po- ste- ri- us, Ga- bri- e-
41
-lis ab o- re su- mens il- lud A- ve, pec- ca- to-
-lis ab o- re su- mens il- lud A- ve, pec- ca-
-lis ab o- re su- mens il- lud A- ve, pec- ca-
-lis ab o- re su- mens il- lud A- ve, pec- ca-

-rum mi- se- re- re, pec- ca- to- rum___ mi- se- re-

-to- rum mi- se- re- re,

-to- rum mi- se- re- re,

-to- rum mi- se- re- re,

-re, pec- ca- to- rum, pec- ca- to- rum mi- se- re- re.

pec- ca- to- rum mi- se- re- re, mi- se- re- re.

pec- ca- to- rum mi- se- re- re.

pec- ca- to- rum mi- se- re- re.

2. Anna mater Matris

11
- stri, An- na ma- tro- na no- bil- lis- si- ma, quae jam re- gnat cum an- ge-
-stri, An- na ma- tro- na no- bil- lis- si- ma,
- na ma- tro- na no- bil- lis- si- ma, no- bil- lis- si- ma,
no- stri, An- na ma- tro- na no- bil- lis- si- ma,
-stri, An- na ma- tro- na no- bil- lis- si- ma,
16
-lis, co- ro- na- ta, co- ro- na- ta in glo- ri- a,
quae jam re- gnat cum an- ge- lis, co- ro-
quae jam re- gnat cum an- ge- lis, co- ro- na- ta in glo- ri- a, co- ro-
quae jam re- gnat cum an- ge- lis, co- ro-
quae jam re- gnat cum an- ge- lis, co- ro-

21
-na- ta in glo- ri- a, co- ro- na- ta in glo- ri- a, i-
-na- ta in glo- ri- a, co- ro- na- - ta in glo- ri- a,
-na- ta in glo- ri- a, co- ro- na- ta in glo- ri- a,
-na- ta in glo- ri- a, co- ro- na- ta in glo- ri- a,
26
i- bi no-
- bi no- stri me- mor e- sto, i- - bi no- stri me- mor e- sto,
i- - bi no- stri me-mor e- sto,
me- mor e- sto, i- bi no- stri me-mor e- sto,
i- - bi no- stri me-mor e- sto,

-stri me- mor, me- mor e- sto. O An-
i- bi no- stri me- mor e- sto.
i- bi no- stri me- mor e- sto.
i- bi no- stri me- mor e- sto.
i- bi no- stri me- mor, me- mor e- sto.

-na san- ctis- si- ma, O An- na san- ctis- si-
O An- na san- ctis- si- ma,
O An- na san- ctis- si- ma, O An-
O An- na san- ctis- si- ma,
O An- na san- ctis- si- ma,

-ma, san-ctis- si- ma, fun- de pre- ces pro no- bis,

O An- na san-ctis- si- ma, fun- de pre-

-na san-ctis- si- ma, O An- na san-ctis- si- ma, fun- de pre-

O An- na san-ctis- si- ma, fun- de pre-

O An- na san-ctis- si- ma, fun- de pre-

pro no- bis,

-ces pro no- bis,

-ces pro no- bis, ut pos- si- mus il- lic tu- o so- ci- a- ri col-

-ces pro no- bis,

-ces pro no- bis,

ut pos-si-mus il-lic tu-o so-ci-a-ri col-le-gi-o,
ut pos-si-mus il-lic tu-o so-ci-a-ri col-le-gi-o, col-le-gi-o, O An- -o.
so-ci-a-ri col-le-gi-o, -o, col-le-gi-o, col-le-gi-o. -o.
ut pos-si-mus il-lic tu-o so-ci-a-ri col-le-gi-o, so-ci-a-ri col-le-gi-o. -o.
-ri col-le-gi-o, col-le-gi-o. -o.
ut pos-si-mus il-lic tu-o so-ci-a-ri col-le-gi-o, col-le-gi-o. -o.

3. Ave Maria (1)

be- ne- di- cta tu in mu- li- e- ri- bus,

be- ne- di- cta tu in mu- li- e- ri- bus, et

-cum, Do- mi- nus te- cum, be- ne- di- cta tu in mu- li- e- ri- bus,

be- ne- di- cta tu in mu- li- e- ri- bus,

be- ne- di- cta tu in mu- li- e- ri- bus,

et be- ne- di-

be- ne- di- ctus fru- ctus ven- tris tu- i, Je- sus, et

et be- ne- di- ctus fru- ctus ven- tris tu- i, Je- sus,

et be- ne- di-

et be- ne- di-

20
-ctus fru- ctus, et be- ne- di- ctus, et be- ne- di- ctus fru-
be- ne- di- ctus, et be- ne- di- ctus fru- ctus ven-
et be- ne- di- - ctus fru-
-ctus fru- ctus, fru- ctus, fru- ctus
-ctus, et be- ne- di- ctus fru- ctus, fru- ctus
24
-ctus ven- tris tu- i, Je- sus.
- tris tu- i, Je- sus. San- cta Ma- ri-
-ctus ven- tris tu- i, Je- sus. San- cta Ma- ri- a, Ma-
ven- tris tu- - i, Je- sus. San- cta Ma- ri- - a, Ma- ri-
ven- tris tu- i, Je- sus. San- cta Ma-

29
San- cta Ma- ri- - a, Ma- ri- a, Ma- ter
- a, San- cta Ma- ri- a, Ma- ri- a, Ma- ter
-ri- a, Ma- ri- a, San- cta Ma- ri- a, Ma- ter
-a, San- cta Ma- ri- a, Ma- ri- a, Ma- ter
-ri- a, Ma- ter
34
De- i, o- ra pro no- bis,
De- i, o- ra pro no- bis, o- ra pro no- bis pec- ca- to- ri-
De- i, o- ra pro no- bis, o- ra pro no- bis pec- ca- to- ri-
De- i, o- ra pro no- bis, o- ra pro no- bis pec- ca- to- ri-
De- i, o- ra pro no- bis,

39
o- ra pro no- bis, o- ra pro no- bis pec- ca- to- ri-
-bus, o- ra pro no- bis, o- ra pro no- bis pec- ca- to- ri-
-bus, o- ra pro no- bis, o- ra pro no- bis pec- ca- to- ri-
-bus, o- ra pro no- bis, o- ra pro no- bis, pro no- bis pec- ca- to- ri-
o- ra pro no- bis,
44
-bus, pro no- bis pec- - ca- to- ri- bus,
-bus, pro no- bis pec- ca- to- ri- bus, nunc et in ho- ra
-bus, pro no- bis, pro no- bis pec- ca- to- ri- bus,
-bus, pro no- bis pec- ca- to- ri- bus,
pro no- bis pec- ca- to- ri- bus,

49
mor- tis no- - strae, nunc et in ho- ra mor- tis, mor- tis no-
nunc et in ho- ra mor- tis no-
nunc et in ho- ra mor- tis no- strae,
nunc
54
nunc et in ho- ra
-strae, nunc
-strae, nunc et in ho- ra mor- tis no- strae, nunc et in
nunc et in ho- ra mor- tis no- strae, ho-
et in ho- ra mor- tis no- - strae, nunc et in

mor- tis, ho- ra mor- tis no- strae,

et in ho- ra mor- tis no- strae, mor- tis no- strae, ho- ra

ho- ra mor- tis no- strae, mor- tis no- strae, ho - ra

- ra mor- tis no- strae, mor- tis no- strae, ho- ra

ho- ra mor- tis no- strae, mor- tis no- strae, ho - ra

ho- ra mor- tis no- strae. A- - men.

mor- tis no- strae. A- men.

mor- tis no- strae. A- men.

mor- tis no- strae. A- men.

mor- tis no- strae. A- men.

4. Ave Maria (2)

15
et be- ne- di- ctus fru- ctus ven- tris tu- i, et be- ne- di- ctus
-tris tu- i, fru- ctus ven- - tris tu- i, et be- ne- di- ctus fru- ctus
ven- tris tu- - i, fru- ctus ven- tris,
et be- ne- di- ctus fru- ctus ven- tris tu- i, et be- ne- di-
19
fru- ctus ven- tris tu- i, et be- ne- di- ctus fru- ctus ven- tris
ven- tris tu- i, et be- ne- di- ctus fru- ctus ven- tris
et be- ne- di- ctus fru- ctus, fru- ctus ven- tris
-ctus fru- ctus, et be- ne- di- ctus fru- ctus, fru- ctus ven- tris
23
tu- i, Je- sus. San- cta Ma- ri- a, Ma- ri- - a,
tu- i, Je- sus. San- cta Ma- ri- a,
tu- i, Je- sus. San- cta Ma- ri- a, Ma-
tu- i, Je- sus. San- cta Ma- ri- a, Ma-

28
Ma- ter De- i, o- ra pro no- bis pec- ca- to- ri- bus, o- ra pro no-
Ma- ter De- i, o- ra pro no- bis pec- ca- to- ri- bus, o- ra pro no-
- ter De- i, o- ra pro no- bis, pro
- ter De- i, o- ra pro no-
33
-bis, pro no- bis pec- ca- to- ri- bus, nunc et in ho- ra mor- tis,
-bis, pro no- bis pec- - ca- to- ri- bus, nunc et in ho- ra
no- bis pec- ca- to- ri- bus,
-bis, pro no- bis pec- ca- to- ri- bus,
38
mor- tis no- strae, nunc et in ho-
mor- tis no- strae, nunc et in ho- ra mor- tis no- strae, nunc et in ho-
nunc et in ho- ra mor- tis no- strae, nunc et in ho-
nunc et in ho- ra mor- tis no- strae, nunc et in ho-

23

5. Ave per cor suavissimum Jesu

-sti. Gau- de- o de tu- a glo- ri- a et lau- do De- um:
-o, gau- de- o de tu- a glo- ri- a et lau- do De- um: Il- lic-
-sti. Gau- de- o de tu- a glo- ri- a et lau- do De- um:
-o, gau- de- o de tu- a glo- ri- a et lau- do De- um:

Il- lic- que pro te of- fe- ro dul- cis- si- mum cor Je- su, il- lic- que
-que pro te of- fe- ro, of- fe- ro dul- cis- si- mum cor Je- su, il- lic- que
Il- lic- que
Il- lic- que

pro te of- fe- ro dul- cis- si- mum cor Je- su, cor Je-
pro te of- fe- ro dul- cis- si- mum cor Je- su, Je- su, cor Je-
pro te of- fe- ro dul- cis- si- mum cor Je- su, cor Je- su.
pro te of- fe- ro dul- cis- si- mum cor Je- su, cor Je- su.

-su. E- ja ergo sponsa Christi,
-su. E- ja er- go sponsa
E- ja ergo sponsa Christi, e- ja ergo
E-

e- ja er- go sponsa Christi gloriosa.
Christi, sponsa Christi gloriosa.
sponsa Christi, sponsa Christi gloriosa.
- ja ergo sponsa Christi gloriosa.

O- ra pro no- bis Dominum, pro no- bis, pro
O- ra pro nobis Dominum
O- ra pro nobis, pro
O- ra pro nobis

45
no- bis Do- mi- num ut om- ni- no fi-
ut om- ni- no, ut om- ni- no fi-
no- bis Do- mi- num ut om- ni- no fi- a- mus, ut om- ni-
Do- mi- num ut om- ni- no fi- a- mus, fi- a-
50
-a- mus se- cun- dum, se- cun- dum cor De- i, se-
-a- mus, fi- a- mus se- cun- dum cor De- i, se- cun-
-no fi- a- mus se- cun- dum cor De- i, se-
-mus se- cun- dum, se- cun- dum cor De- i, se- cun-
55
-cun- dum cor De- i. A-
-dum cor De- i.
-cun- dum cor De- i. A- - men, a- -
-dum cor De- i. A- - men, a-

6. Ave Regina caelorum

12
a- - ve Do- mi- na An- ge-
Do- mi- na, Do- - mi- na An- - ge-
Do- mi- na, Do- - mi- na An- ge-
- mi- na, Do- mi- na An- ge-
17
-lo- rum: Sal- ve ra- dix, sal- ve
-lo- rum: Sal- ve ra- dix, sal- ve
-lo- rum:
-lo- rum:
23
por- - ta, Ex qua mun- - do
por- - ta, Ex qua

29
lux est or- - ta:
mun- - do lux est or- ta:
35
Gau- de Vir- go glo- ri- o- sa, gau- de
Gau- de Vir- go glo- ri- o- sa, gau- de
Gau- de Vir- go glo- ri- o- sa, gau- de
Gau- de Vir- go glo- ri- o- sa, gau- de
40
Vir- go glo- ri- o- sa, Su- per om- nes spe- ci- o-
Vir- go glo- ri- o- sa,
Vir- go glo- ri- o- sa,
Vir- go glo- ri- o- sa,

31

7. Ave salus mundi

19
ver- - bum pa- - tris, ho- - sti- a
pa- - tris, ho- - sti- a sa- -
- bum pa- tris, ho- - - sti- a
ver- bum pa- - tris, ho- - sti- a
26
sa- cra, Ve-
- cra, Ve- ra vi- - va, vi-
sa- cra, Ve- - ra vi- va, vi- va ca-
sa- cra, Ve- - ra vi-
33
-ra vi- va ca- ro, De- i- tas in- - te-
-va ca- ro, De- - i- tas in- - te-
- - ro, De- i- tas in- - te- gra,
-va ca- ro, De- i- tas in- - te- gra,

40
-gra, ve- rus ho- mo:
-gra, ve- - - - rus ho- mo:
ve- - - rus ho- mo:
ve- - - rus ho- mo: Cor-
46
Cor- pus Do- - mi- ni no- stri Je- - su
Je- su, Je- - su
Cor- pus Do- - mi- ni no- - stri Je- su
- pus Do- - mi- ni no- stri Je- - su
53
Chri- sti qui me for- ma- sti,
Chri- sti qui me for- ma- sti,
Chri- sti qui me for- ma- sti, tu mi- se-
Chri- sti qui me for- ma- sti, tu

60
tu mi- se- re- re
tu mi- se- re- re, tu mi- se- re-
-re- re me- - i, tu mi- se- re-
mi- se- re- re me- i, tu mi- se- re-
66
me- - i. A- men.
- - re me- i. A- men.
- re me- - i. A- - men.
- re me- i. A- men.

8. Ave virginum gemma Catharina

16
-va, vi- va Chri- sti ho- sti- a. Tu- - a ve- ne-
- ve vi- va Chri- sti ho- sti- a. Tu- a ve- ne-
-va, vi- va Chri- sti ho- sti- a. Tu- a ve- - ne- ran-
-va, vi- va Chri- sti ho- sti- a. Tu- a ve- - ne- ran-
21
-ran- ti- bus pa- tro- ci- ni- a, pa- tro- ci- ni- a im- pe-
-ran- ti- bus pa- tro- ci- ni- a, pa- tro- ci- ni- a im- pe- tra- ta non
- ti- bus pa- tro- ci- ni- a im- pe- tra-
- ti- bus pa- tro- ci- ni- a, pa- tro- ci- ni- a im- pe-
26
-tra- ta non de- ne- ges suf- fra- gi- a, im- pe- tra- ta, im- pe-
de- ne- ges, non de- ne- ges suf- fra- gi- a, im- pe- tra-
- ta non de- ne- ges suf- fra- gi- a, im- pe- tra- ta non de- ne-
-tra- ta non de- ne- ges suf- fra- gi- a, im- pe- tra- ta non

31
-tra- ta non de- ne- ges suf- fra- gi- a, non de- ne- ges suf- fra- gi- a, suf-
-ta non de- ne- ges, non de- ne- ges, non de- ne- ges, de- ne-
-ges, non de- ne- ges suf- fra- - gi- a, non de- ne- ges suf-
de- ne- ges suf- fra- gi- a, non de- ne- ges, non de- ne-
35
-fra- gi- a. A- - -
-ges suf- fra- gi- a. A-
-fra- gi- a.
-ges suf- fra- gi- a.
40
- men, a- men, a- - - men.
- - men, a- - - men.
A- - - men.
A- - - men.

9. Benedicimus te

10
-i in lau- dem tu- am no- bis, in lau-dem tu- am no-
-i in lau- dem tu- am no-
-i in lau- dem tu- am no-
-i in lau- dem tu- am no-
-i in lau- dem tu- am no-
15
-bis ex- pen- de- re tri- bu- i- sti. Te- que sup- pli- ci- ter ex- o-
-bis ex- pen- de- re tri- bu- i- sti.
-bis ex- pen- de- re tri- bu- i- sti.
-bis ex- pen- de- re tri- bu- i- sti.
-bis ex- pen- de- re tri- bu- i- sti.

20
-ra- mus, te- - que sup- pli- ci-
Te- que sup- pli- ci- ter ex- o- ra- mus,
Te- que sup- pli- ci- ter ex- o- ra- mus,
Te- que sup- pli- ci- ter ex- o- ra- mus,
Te- que sup- pli- ci- ter ex- o- ra- mus,
25
-ter ex- o- ra- mus
te- que sup- pli- ci- ter ex- o- ra-
te- que sup- pli- ci- ter ex- o- ra-
te- que sup- pli- ci- ter ex- o- ra-
te- que sup- pli- ci- ter ex- o- ra-

ut san- ctis tu- is qui- bus ho- no- ri- fi- cen-
-mus ut sanctis tu- is qui- bus, qui- bus
-mus ut san- ctis tu- is qui- bus
-mus ut san- ctis tu- is qui- bus
-mus ut sanctis tu- is qui- bus

-ti- am ex- hi- be- mus
ho- no- ri- fi- cen- ti-
ho- no- ri- fi- cen- ti- am
ho- no- ri- fi- cen- ti- am ex- hi- be- mus, ho- no- ri- fi- cen- ti-
ho- no- ri- fi- cen- ti-

38
virtu- te ac pre-
-am ex- hi- be- mus, ex- hi- be- mus vir- tu- te
ex- hi- be- mus, ex- hi- be- mus vir- tu- te
-am ex- hi- be- mus, ex- hi- be- mus vir- tu- te
-am ex- hi- be- mus, ex- hi- be- mus vir- tu- te
43
- mi- o so- ci- a- ri me- re- a-
ac pre- - mi- o
ac pre- - mi- o
ac pre- - mi- o
ac pre- - mi- o

10. Domine salvum fac regem (1)

5
-gem, Do- mi- ne, Do- mi- ne sal- vum, sal- vum fac re- gem, Do- mi-
-gem,
-gem, Do- mi- ne, Do- mi- ne sal- vum, sal- vum, sal- vum fac re- gem,
Do- mi- ne,
-gem, Do- mi-
9
-ne sal- vum, sal- vum fac re- gem: et ex-
Do- mi- ne sal- vum, sal- vum fac re- - gem, re- gem:
Do- mi- ne sal- vum fac re- gem, fac re- gem: et ex- au- di nos in di-
Do- mi- ne sal- vum fac re- gem:
-ne, Do- mi- ne sal- vum fac re- gem, fac re- gem: et ex- au- di

14
-au- di nos in di- - e, et ex- au- di nos in di- e, in
et ex- au- di nos in di- e,
- e, nos in di- e, in di- e, in
et ex- au- di nos in di- e, et ex- au- di
nos in di- e, et ex- au- di nos in di- e, in
18
di- e qua in- vo- ca- ve- ri- mus, qua in- vo- ca- ve- ri-
in di- e qua in- vo- ca-
di- e
nos in di- e
di- e

22
-mus, qua in- vo- ca- ve- ri- mus, qua in- vo- ca- - ve- ri- mus, qua in- vo- ca-
-ve- ri- mus, in- vo- ca- ve- ri- mus te, in- vo- ca- ve-
qua in- vo- ca- ve- ri- mus, in- vo-
qua in- vo- ca-
26
1.
2.
-ve- ri- mus te, in- vo- ca- ve- - ri- mus te, te.
- ri- mus te, in- vo- ca- ve- ri- mus te, te.
- ca- ve- ri- mus, in- vo- ca- ve- ri- mus te, et ex- te.
-ve- ri- mus te, in- vo- ca- ve- - ri- mus te, te.
qua in- vo- ca- ve- ri- mus, in- vo- ca- ve- ri- mus te, te.

11. Domine salvum fac regem (2)

13
et ex- au- di nos in di- e, in di-
- e, nos in di- e, et ex- au- di nos in di-
et ex- au- di nos in di- e,
nos in di- e, et ex- au- di nos in di-
17
-e, in di- e qua in- vo- ca- ve- ri- mus, in- vo- ca- ve- ri- mus
-e, in di- e qua in- vo- ca-
in di- e
-e, in di- e
21
te, qua in- vo- ca- ve- ri- mus, in- vo- ca- ve- - ri- mus te, qua in- vo- ca-
-ve- ri- mus, in- vo- ca- ve- ri- mus te, qua
qua in- vo- ca- ve- ri- mus, in- vo-

12. Domine salvum fac regem (3)

4
-gem, Do- mi- ne, Do- mi- ne sal- vum, sal-
-ne, Do- mi- ne sal- vum fac re- gem, sal-
Do- mi- ne sal- vum, sal- vum fac re- gem, Do- mi- ne, Do- mi- ne sal- vum, sal-
-ne sal- vum, sal- vum fac re- gem, sal-
-ne sal- vum, sal- vum fac re- gem, sal-
8
-vum, sal- vum fac re- gem: et ex- au- di
-vum, sal- vum fac re- gem:
-vum fac re- gem, fac re- gem:
-vum, sal- vum fac re- gem: et ex- au- di nos in
-vum, sal- vum fac re- gem:

12
nos in di- e, et ex- au- di
et ex- au- di nos in di- e, in di-
et ex- au- di nos, et ex- au- di nos in di- e,
di- e, in di- e, et ex- au- di nos in di-
et ex- au- di nos in di- e, in di-
16
nos in di- e, in di- e qua in- vo- ca- ve- ri- mus
-e, in di- e, in di- e
in di- e, in di- e
-e, in di- e, in di- e qua in- vo- ca- ve- ri- mus, qua in- vo- ca-
-e, in di- e, in di- e

20
te, in- vo- ca- ve- - ri- mus te,
qua in- vo- ca-
qua in- vo- ca- ve- ri- mus te,
-ve- ri- mus te, in- vo- ca- ve- ri- mus te, in-
qua in- vo- ca- ve- ri- mus te, in- vo- ca- ve- ri- mus te, in-
24
qua in- vo- ca- ve- ri- mus te.
-ve- ri- mus te, in- vo- ca- ve- ri- mus te.
in- vo- ca- ve- - ri- mus, in- vo- ca- ve- ri- mus te.
-vo- ca- ve- ri- mus, in- vo- ca- ve- ri- mus te. Do- mi-
-vo- ca- ve- ri- mus te, in- vo- ca- ve- ri- mus te.

28
Do- mi- ne sal-
sal- vum, sal- vum fac re- gem,
sal- vum fac re- gem, fac re- gem,
-ne sal- vum fac re- gem, sal- vum fac re- gem,
Do- mi- ne sal- vum, sal- vum, sal- vum fac re- gem,
32
-vum, sal- vum fac re- gem, fac re- gem:
sal- vum fac re- gem:
Do- mi- ne sal- vum, sal- vum fac re- gem, sal- vum fac re- gem.
Do- mi- ne sal- vum fac re- gem: et ex-
Do- mi- ne sal- vum fac re- gem.

37
et ex- au- di nos in di- e, et ex-
et ex- au- di nos in
et ex- au- di nos, et ex- au- di nos in
-au- di nos in di- e, in di- e, et ex- au- di nos
et ex- au- di nos in di- e, in

41
-au- di nos in di- e, in di- e
di- e, in di- e, in di- e, in di- e
di- e, in di- e, in di- e
in di- e, in di- e, in di- e qua in- vo- ca-
di- e, in di- e, in di- e

qua in-vo-ca-ve-ri-mus te, in-vo-ca-ve-ri-mus te,

-ve-ri-mus, qua in-vo-ca-ve-ri-mus te, in-vo-ca-ve-ri-

qua in-vo-ca-ve-ri-mus te, in-vo-ca-ve-ri-mus

qua in-vo-ca-ve-ri-mus te.

qua in-vo-ca-ve-ri-mus te, in-vo-ca-ve-ri-mus te.

te, in-vo-ca-ve-ri-mus, in-vo-ca-ve-ri-mus te.

-mus te, in-vo-ca-ve-ri-mus, in-vo-ca-ve-ri-mus te.

te, in-vo-ca-ve-ri-mus te, in-vo-ca-ve-ri-mus te.

13. Domine salvum fac regem (4)

12
qua in- vo- ca- ve- ri- mus, in- vo- ca- ve- ri- mus te, in- vo- ca- ve- ri- mus, in- vo- ca-
qua in- vo- ca- ve- ri- mus, in- vo- ca- ve- ri- mus, in- vo- ca- ve-
16
-ve- ri- mus te, qua in- vo- ca- ve- ri- mus te, in- vo- ca- ve- ri-
- ri- mus te,
qua in- vo- ca- ve- ri- mus, in- vo- ca- ve- ri- mus
qua in- vo- ca- ve- ri- mus, in- vo- ca- ve- ri- mus
20
-mus te, qua in- vo- ca- ve- ri- mus te.
qua in- vo- ca- ve- - ri- mus te, in- vo- ca- ve- ri- mus te.
te, qua in- vo- ca- ve- ri- mus, in- vo- ca- ve- ri- mus te.
te, qua in- vo- ca- ve- ri- mus, in- vo- ca- ve- ri- mus te.

14. Duo seraphim

*For an alternative setting of the opening, see no. 14a.

17
San- ctus, San- -
San- - - ctus, San- ctus, San-
San- ctus, San- - ctus, San-
San- ctus, San- - - ctus, San-
24
- - ctus, San- - - - ctus
- - ctus, San- ctus Do-
- ctus, San- - - ctus
-ctus, San- - - - ctus
31
Do- mi- nus De- - - us Sa- ba- oth. Ple-
- mi- nus De- us, De- - us Sa- ba- oth. Ple-
Do- - mi- nus De- - us Sa- ba- oth. Ple-
Do- mi- nus De- us, De- us Sa- ba- oth. Ple-

38
- na est om- - nis ter- ra glo- ri- a
-na est om- - nis te- - ra
-na est om- nis ter- ra glo- - ri-
-na est om- - nis ter- ra glo- - ri-
45
e- - jus, glo- ri- a e- -
glo- - - ri- a e- - jus,
-a e- jus, glo- - ri- a e-
-a e- jus, glo- - ri- a e- jus, glo-
52
- - - - jus. Tres sunt qui
glo- ri- a e- jus. Tres sunt qui
- - - - jus. Tres sunt qui
- ri- a e- - jus.
[Fine]

60
te- sti- mo- ni- um dant in cae- lo:
te- sti- mo- ni- um dant in cae- - lo:
te- sti- mo- ni- um dant in cae- lo:
67
Pa- ter, Ver- bum, et Spi- ri- tus San- ctus:
Pa- ter, Ver- bum, et Spi- ri- tus San- ctus: et
Pa- ter, Ver- bum, et Spi- ri- tus San- ctus:
73
et hi tres u- num sunt, et hi tres u- - num sunt.
hi tres u- - num sunt, u- - num, u- num sunt.
et hi tres u- num sunt, u- num sunt.
D.S. al Fine

14a. Duo seraphim (alternative opening)

*Music continues with no. 14, measure 17.

15. Ecce panis Angelorum

-rum: Ve- re pa- nis fi- li- o- rum,

-rum: Ve- re pa- nis fi- li- o- rum, Non mit- ten- dus ca- ni- bus,

Ve- re pa- nis fi- li- o- rum, Non mit-

-rum: Ve- re pa- nis fi- li- o- rum, Non mit- ten- dus ca- ni- bus, non

-rum: Ve- re pa- nis fi- li- o- rum, Non mit- ten-

Non mit- ten- dus ca- ni- bus.

non mit- ten- dus, non mit- ten- dus ca- ni- bus, ca- ni- bus.

-ten- dus ca- ni- bus, non mit- ten- dus ca- ni- bus.

mit- ten- dus ca- ni- bus, non mit- ten- dus ca- ni- bus.

-dus ca- ni- bus, ca- ni- bus, non mit- ten- dus ca- ni- bus.

16. Fons aquae vivae

15
-ja, al- le- lu- ja, al- le- lu- ja: Et sic- ut flo- res, et
-ja, al- le- lu- ja, al- le- lu- ja: Et sic-
-ja, al- le- lu- ja, al- le- lu- ja: Et sic- ut flo-
-ja, al- le- lu- ja, al- le- lu- ja: Et sic- ut flo-
20
sic- ut flo- res pa- ra- di- si ri- ga- vit nos,
-ut flo- res pa- ra- di- si ri- ga- vit nos, al- le- lu- ja, al- le- lu-
-res pa- ra- di- si, pa- ra- di- si ri- ga- vit nos,
-res pa- ra- di- si ri- ga- vit nos,
25
al- le- lu- ja, al- le- lu- ja, al- le- lu- ja.
-ja, al- le- lu- ja, al- le- lu- ja.
al- le- lu- ja, al- le- lu- ja, al- le- lu- ja. Ut in a- mo-
al- le- lu- ja, al- le- lu- ja, al- le- lu- ja.

30
Ut in a- mo- re Je- - su, Je- su, ut in a- mo- - re Je-
Ut in a- mo- - re Je-
- re Je- - su, Je- su, ut in a- mo- re
Ut in a- mo- re Je- su,
35
- su flo- re- scant a- ni- mae san- cto- rum, flo- re- scant a- ni-
-su, Je- su flo- re- scant a- ni- mae san- cto- rum, flo- re- scant a- ni-
Je- su flo- re- scant a- ni- mae san- cto- rum, flo- re- scant a- ni-
Je- su flo- re- scant a- ni- mae san- cto- rum, flo- re- scant a- ni-
40
-mae san- cto- rum, Et li- li- a, et li- li- a, et li- li-
-mae san- cto- rum, Et li- li- a Vir-
-mae san- cto- rum, Et li- li- a, et li-
-mae san- cto- rum, Et li- li- a

-a Vir- gi- num su- a- vi- ta- tis o- do- ris in- fun-
- gi- num su- a- vi- ta- tis o- do- ris in- fun-
- li- a Vir- gi- num su- a- vi- ta- tis o- do- ris in- fun-
Vir- gi- num su- a- vi- ta- tis o- do- ris in- fun-

-dant. O Je- su fons a- mo- ris, o Je- su, o
-dant. O Je- su, o
-dant. O Je- su fons a- mo- ris, o
-dant. O Je- su, o Je- su, o

Je- su fons a- mo- ris, in- fun- de ro- ram gra- ti- a-
Je- su fons a- mo- ris, a- mo- ris, in- fun- de ro- ram gra- ti- a- rum,
Je- su fons a- mo- ris, in- fun-
Je- su fons a- mo- ris, in- fun- de ro-

60
-rum, gra- ti- a- rum, gra- ti- a- rum,
gra- ti- a- - - rum, gra- ti- a- rum,
-de ro- ram gra- - ti- a- rum, gra- ti- a- rum, Et
-ram, ro- ram gra- ti- a- rum, gra- ti- a- rum,
65
Et in o- do- rem unguen- to- rum, un- guen- to- rum i- bi-
Et in o- do- rem un-guen-to-
in o- do- rem un- - guen- to- - rum, un- guen- to-
Et in o- do- rem un- guen- to-
70
-mus, i- bi- mus, Et lae- tan- tis can- ta- bi- mus, can- ta- bi- mus, et lae-
- rum i- bi- mus, Et lae- tan- tis can- ta- bi- mus, can- ta- bi- mus,
- rum i- bi- mus, Et lae- tan- tis can- ta- bi- mus, can- ta- bi- mus,
- rum i- bi- mus, Et lae- tan- tis can- ta- bi- mus, can- ta- bi- mus,

75
-tan- tis can- ta- bi- mus, et lae- tan- tis can- ta- - bi- mus, et lae-
et lae- tan- tis can- ta- - bi- mus,
et lae- tan- tis can- ta- bi- mus, can- - ta- bi- mus,
et lae- tan- tis can- ta- - bi- mus,
79
-tan- tis can- ta- bi- mus, can- ta- bi- mus, can- ta- bi-
can- ta- bi- mus, can- ta- bi- mus, can-
can- ta- bi- mus, can-
can- ta- bi- mus, can- ta- bi-
83
-mus, can- ta- bi- mus, al- le- lu- ja, al- - le- lu- ja.
- ta- bi- mus, al- - le- lu- ja.
-ta- bi- mus, al- - le- lu- ja.
-mus, can- ta- bi- mus, al- - le- lu- ja.

17. Hic est beatissimus

13
-le- gi- o a- mo- ris, a- mo- ris prae- ci- pu- i, a- mo- - ris
Cum pri- vi- le- gi- o a- mo- ris, a- mo-
pri- vi- le- gi- o a- mo- ris, a- mo- ris, a- mo-
Cum pri- vi- le- gi- o a- mo- ris, a- mo- ris prae-
17
prae- ci- pu- i cae- te- ris al- ti- us a Do- mi-
- ris prae- ci- pu- i cae- te- ris al- ti- us a Do- mi-
-ris prae- ci- pu- i cae- te- ris al- ti- us a Do- mi-
-ci- pu- i cae- te- ris al- ti- us a Do- mi-
21
-no me- ru- i- sti ho- no- ra- ri, me- ru- i- sti ho- no- ra-
-no me- ru- i- sti ho- no- ra- ri, me- ru- i- sti ho- no- ra-
-no me- ru- i- sti, me- ru- i- sti ho- no- ra- ri, me- ru- i- sti ho- no- ra-
-no me- ru- i- sti ho- - no- ra- ri, me- ru- i- sti ho- no- ra-

-ri. Hic est discipulus ille quem diligebat Je-
-ri.
-ri.
-ri.

-sus qui super pectus Domini in caena recubu-
qui super pectus Domini in caena, in caena, in caena recubu-

-it. Cum privilegio amoris, amoris, amoris prae-
Cum privilegio amoris, amoris
-it. Cum privilegio amoris, amoris prae-
Cum privilegio amoris, amoris prae-

41
- ci- pu- i cae- te- ris al- ti- us a Do- mi- no me- ru-
prae- ci- pu- i cae- te- ris al- ti- us a Do- mi- no me- ru-
-ci- pu- i cae- te- ris al- ti- us a Do- mi- no me- ru-
-ci- pu- i cae- te- ris al- ti- us a Do- mi- no me- ru-
46
-i- sti ho- no- ra- ri, me- ru- i- sti ho- no- ra- ri.
-i- sti ho- no- ra- ri, me- ru- i- sti ho- no- ra- ri.
-i- sti, me- ru- i- sti ho- no- ra- ri, me- ru- i- sti ho- no- ra- ri.
-i- sti ho- - no- ra- ri, me- ru- i- sti ho- no- ra- ri.

18. O athletum invictissimum

77

au- di- re, au- di- re me- ru- it, me- ru- it,

-re vi- a- ti- cum, au-

-a- ti- cum, au- di- re, au- di- re me- ru- it, me- ru- it, au-

-re vi- a- ti- cum, au-

-a- ti- cum, au-

ne me- tu- as, qui- a ad

-di- re, au- di- re me- ru- it, ne me- tu- as,

-di- re, au- di- re me- ru- it, ne me- tu- as,

-di- re, au- di- re me- ru- it, ne me- tu- as,

-di- re, au- di- re me- ru- it, ne me- tu- as,

patriam caelestum te transferam

qui a ad patriam caelestum te transfe-

qui a ad patriam caelestum te transfe-

qui a ad patriam caelestum te transfe-

qui a ad patriam caelestum te transfe-

-ram quo laureatus exultes, exultes, exul-

-ram quo laurea-

-ram quo laureatus exul-

-ram quo laureatus exultes, ex-

-ram quo laureatus exul-

44
-tes, ex- ul- tes, quo lau- re- a- tus, ex- ul- tes, ex- ul-
-tus ex- ul- tes
-tes, ex- ul- tes, quo lau- re- a- tus ex- ul- tes, ex- - ul-
- ul- tes, quo lau- re- a- tus ex- ul-
-tes, ex- ul- tes, quo lau- re- a- tus ex- ul-
49
-tes, quo lau- re- a- tus ex- ul- tes.
quo lau- re- a- tus ex- ul- tes.
-tes, quo lau- re- a- - tus ex- ul- tes.
-tes, quo lau- re- a- tus ex- ul- tes, quo lau- re- a- tus ex- ul- tes.
-tes, quo lau- re- a- tus ex- ul- tes, ex- ul- tes.

81

19. O crux ave

21
- ge pi- is, au- - ge pi- is ju- sti- -
Au- - ge pi- is ju- sti-
Au- - ge pi-
Au- ge pi- is ju-
28
- - ti- am, Re- is- que do- na,
- - ti- am, Re- - is-
-is ju- sti- ti- am, Re- is- que do- - na ve- ni-
-sti- - ti- am, Re- is- que do- na, re-
35
re- is- que do- na ve- ni- am.
-que do- - - na ve- - ni- am.
-am, re- is- que do- - na ve- - ni- am.
-is- que do- na, do- - na ve- ni- am.

20. O Doctor optime

10
-ae, Ec- cle- si- ae, Ec- cle- si- ae san- ctae lu- men,
-ae, Ec- cle- si- ae, Ec- cle- si- ae san- ctae lu- men,
Ec- cle- si- ae san- - ctae lu- men, be-
-ae, Ec- cle- si- ae, Ec- cle- si- ae san- ctae lu- men,
-ae, Ec- cle- si- ae, Ec- cle- si- ae san- ctae lu- men,
15
be- a- te Au- gu- sti- ne, di-
be- a- te Au- - gu- sti- ne,
-a- te Au- - gu- sti- ne, Au- gu- sti- ne, di-
be- a- te Au- gu- sti- ne,
be- a- te Au- gu- sti- ne,

20
-vi- nae le- gis a- ma- tor, le- gis a- ma- tor,
di- vi- nae le- gis a- ma- tor, di- vi- nae le- gis a- ma-
-vi- nae le- gis a- ma- - tor, di- vi- nae le- gis a- ma-
di- vi- nae le- gis a- ma- tor,
di- vi- nae, di- vi- nae le- gis a- ma- tor,
25
a- ma- tor: de- pre- ca- re pro no- bis,
-tor, a- ma- tor: de- pre- ca- re pro
-tor, a- ma- tor: de- pre- ca- re, de- pre- ca- re pro
a- ma- tor: de- pre- ca- re pro
a- ma- tor: de- pre- ca- re pro

30
de- pre- ca- re,
no- bis, de- pre- ca- re pro no- bis Fi- - li- um De- i, de- pre-
no- bis, de- pre- ca- re
no- bis, de- pre- ca- re pro no- bis, de- pre-
no- bis, de- pre- ca- re, de- pre-
35
de- pre- ca- re pro no- bis Fi- - li- um De- i. de- pre-
-ca- re pro no- bis Fi- li- um De- i, Fi- li- um De- i.
pro no- - bis Fi- li- um, Fi- li- um De- i.
-ca- re pro no- bis Fi- li- um, Fi- li- um De- i.
-ca- re pro no- bis Fi- li- um, Fi- li- um De- i.
1.

88

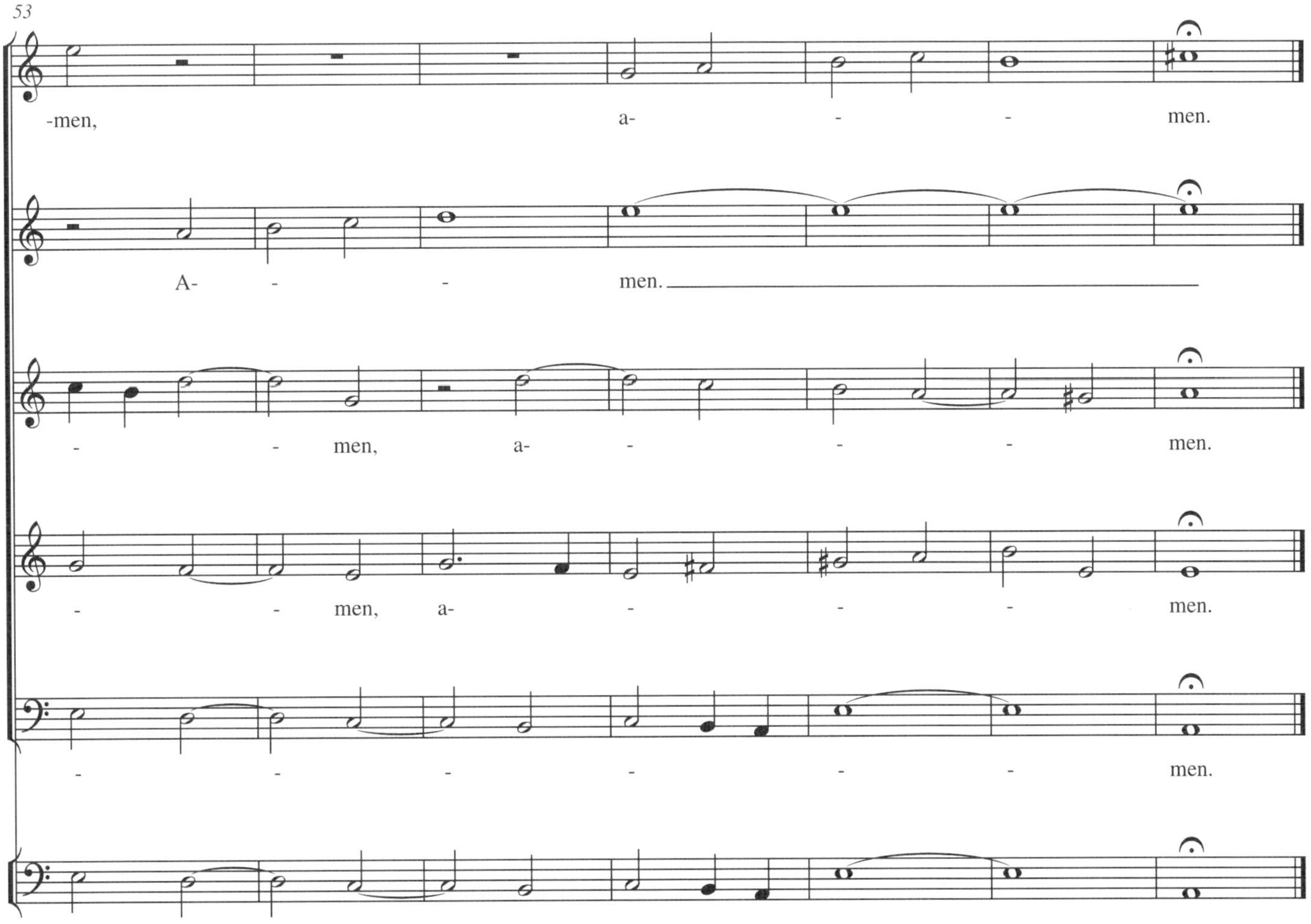
53
-men, a- - - men.
A- - - men.
- - men, a- - - - men.
- - men, a- - - - men.
- - - - - - men.

21. O Pastor aeterne

-re, vo- ce la- psa de cae- lo, de cae-
-re, vo- ce la- psa de cae- lo, vo- ce la- psa de cae-
-re,
-re,
-lo prae- su- li san- ctis- si- mo, prae- su- li san- ctis- si- mo, di-
-lo prae- su- li san- ctis- si- mo, prae- su- li san- ctis- si- mo, di-
prae- su- li san- ctis- si- mo, di-
prae- su- li san- ctis- si- mo, di-
-gnum E- pi- sco- pa- tum Ni- co- la- um, Ni- co- la- um,
-gnum E- pi- sco- pa- tum Ni- co- la- um, Ni- co- la- um,
-gnum E- pi- sco- pa- tum Ni- co- la- um, Ni- co- la- um,
-gnum E- pi- sco- pa- tum Ni- co- la- um, Ni- co- la- um, o-

30
o- sten- di- - sti tan- - tum fa- mu- lum. A-
o- sten- di- sti tan- tum fa- mu- lum.
o- sten- di- sti tan- tum fa- mu- lum.
- sten- di- - sti tan- tum fa- mu- lum.

35
- men, a- - - men.
A- - - - men.
A- - men.
A- - - men.

22. O quam suavis

-o replesti suavissimo, O tuo replesti suavissimo. cibo tuo replesti suavissimo. tuo replesti suavissimo, sua-

-bone Jesu, o bone Jesu, salvum fac sponsam tuam, con- O bone Jesu, salvum fac sponsam tuam, O bone Jesu, salvum, salvum fac sponsam tuam, -vissimo. O bone Jesu, salvum fac sponsam tuam,

-serva populum, populum tuum, et da nobis pacem, et da nobis pacem, et da nobis, et da et da nobis pacem, et da nobis pacem,

33
et vi- tam ae- ter- nam, et vi- tam ae- ter- nam, et
no- bis pa- cem, et vi- tam ae- ter- nam, et vi- tam ae- ter-
et vi- tam ae- ter- - nam, et vi- tam ae-
et vi- tam ae- ter- nam, et vi- tam ae-
38
vi- tam ae- ter- nam, et vi- tam ae- ter- nam. A- men.
- nam, et vi- - tam ae- ter- nam. A- men.
-ter- nam, et vi- tam ae- ter- nam, ae- ter- nam. A- men.
-ter- nam, et vi- tam ae- ter- nam, ae- ter- nam. A- men.

23. O sacrum convivium

15
— im- ple- tur gra- ti- a, mens — im- ple- tur gra- ti- a: et fu-
et fu-
mens im- ple- tur gra- ti- a, gra- ti- a: et fu-
20
-tu- rae glo- ri- ae, et fu- tu- rae glo- ri- ae no- bis pi- gnus
-tu- rae glo- ri- ae, glo- ri- ae, glo- ri- ae no- bis pi- gnus, no- bis pi-
-tu- rae glo- ri- ae, et fu- tu- rae, et fu- tu- rae glo- ri- ae no- bis pi-
et fu- tu- rae glo- ri- ae no- bis, no- bis
25
da- tur. Al- le- lu- ja, al- le- lu- ja, al- le- lu- ja, al- le- lu-
-gnus da- tur. Al- le- lu-
-gnus da- tur. Al- le- lu- ja, al- le- lu- ja, al- le- lu-
pi- gnus da- tur. Al- le- lu- ja, al- le- lu- ja, al- le- lu-

24. Popule meus

12
- vi te? re- spon- - de mi- hi.
- vi te? re- spon- de mi- - hi.
-sta- vi te? re- spon- de, re- spon- de mi- hi.
- vi te? re- spon- de mi- hi.
[Fine]
18
Qui- a e- du- xi te de ter- - ra, de
Qui-
Qui- a e- du- - -
Qui- a e-
25
ter- - ra, de ter- ra Ae- gy- pti, Ae-
-a e- du- xi te de ter- ra, de ter- ra Ae-
- xi te de ter- ra, de ter- ra Ae-
-du- - xi te de ter- ra, de ter- ra Ae-

*-gy- pti: pa- ra- sti cru- cem, cru- cem Sal-
*-gy- pti: Sal-
*-gy- pti: pa- ra- sti cru- cem Sal- va- to-
*-gy- pti: pa- ra- sti cru-

-va- to- ri, Sal- va- to- ri tu- o.
-va- to- ri tu- o.
- ri, Sal- va- to- ri tu- o.
-cem Sal- va- to- ri tu- o.

D.C. "Popule meus," etc.

Pro- pter te fla- gel- la- vi,
Pro- pter te fla- gel-
Pro- pter te fla- gel- la- vi Ae-
Pro- pter te fla- gel-

[D.C. "Popule meus," etc.]

25. Pretiosus Domini Dionysius

-mo di- xit: nunc jam Do- mi- ne per co- ro- nam mar- ty- ri- i cum fra- tri- bus me- is ser- vis tu- is su- sci- pe me, su- sci- pe me. Tu- os- que Do- mi- ne mi

36
tu- ae cu- sto- di- ae com- men- do, com- men- do, com- men-
com- men- do, com-
com- men- do, com- men-
com-
41
-do, com- men- do, quos mi- ni- ste- ri- o, mi- ni- ste- - ri- o
-men- do,
-do, com- men- do, quos mi- ni- ste-
-men- do, quos
46
no- stro et ti- bi tu- o san- gui- ne ac- qui- si- sti,
et ti- bi tu- o san- gui- ne ac- qui- si-
- ri- o no- stro et ti- bi tu- o san- gui- ne ac- qui-
mi- ni- ste- ri- o no- stro et ti- bi tu- o san- gui- ne ac- qui-

51
ac- qui- si- sti. Cun- ctos qui te per nos in no- mi-
- sti. Cun- ctos qui te per nos in no- mi- ne, in no- mi-
-si- sti. in no- mi-
-si- sti. in no- mi-
56
-ne tu- o pe- ti- e- rint ut pol- li- ci- tus et cle- men-
-ne tu- o pe- ti- e- rint ut pol- li- ci- tus et cle- men-
-ne tu- o pe- - ti- e- rint ut pol- li- ci- tus et cle- men-
-ne tu- o pe- ti- e- rint ut pol- li- ci- tus et cle- men-
61
-ter ex- au- di, et cle- men- - ter ex- au- di, et cle- men- ter ex- au- di.
-ter ex- au- di, et cle- men- ter ex- au- di, et cle- men- - ter ex- au- di.
-ter ex- au- di, et cle- men- ter ex- au- di.
-ter ex- au- di, et cle- men- ter ex- au- di.

26. Regina caeli (1)

-a quem me- ru- i- sti por- ta- re,

Qui- a quem me- ru- i- sti por- ta-

Qui- a quem me- ru- i- sti por- ta-

Qui- a quem me- ru-

qui- a quem me- ru- i- sti por- ta-

-re, quem me- ru- i- sti por- ta- re, por- ta-

-re, quem me- ru- i- sti por- ta- re, por- ta- re, por- ta-

-i- sti por- ta- re, por- ta-

26
-re, al- le- lu- ja, al- le- lu- ja, al- le- lu- ja, al- le- lu- ja, al- le- lu-
al- le- lu- ja, al- le- lu- ja, al- le- lu- ja,
-re, al- le- lu- ja, al- le- lu-
-re, al- le- lu- ja, al- le- lu-
-re, al- le- lu- ja, al- le- lu- ja, al- le- lu- ja, al- le- lu- ja, al- le- lu-

31
-ja, al- le- lu- ja: Re- sur- re-
al- le- lu- ja: sic- - ut di-
-ja, al- le- lu- ja: Re- sur- re- xit, sic- - ut di-
-ja, al- le- lu- ja: Re- sur- re- xit, sic- ut di-
-ja, al- le- lu- ja: Re- sur- re- xit,

36
-xit, sic- ut di- xit, al- le- lu- ja, al- le- lu- ja, al- le- lu- ja, al- le- lu-
-xit, al- le- lu- ja,
-xit, sic- ut di- xit, al- le- lu- ja, al- le- lu- ja, al- le- lu- ja, al- le- lu-
-xit, sic- ut di- xit, al- le- lu- ja, al- le- lu- ja, al- le- lu- ja, al- le- lu-
sic- ut di- xit, al- le- lu- ja, al- le- lu- ja,
41
-ja, al- le- lu- ja: O- ra pro no- - - bis,
al- le- lu- ja: O- ra pro no- - bis, De-
-ja, al- le- lu- ja:
-ja, al- le- lu- ja:
al- le- lu- ja: O- - - ra pro no- - bis, De- um,

49
De- um, al- le- lu- ja, al- le- lu- ja, al- le- lu- ja, al- le- lu-
- um, al- le- lu- ja, al- le- lu- ja, al- le- lu-
al- le- lu- ja, al- le- lu- ja, al- le- lu- ja,
al- le- lu- ja, al- le- lu- ja, al- le- lu-
al- le- lu- ja, al- le- lu- ja, al- le- lu-
54
-ja, al- le- lu- ja, al- le- lu- ja, al- le- lu- ja, al- le- lu- ja.
-ja, al- le- lu- ja, al- le- lu- ja, al- le- lu- ja.
al- le- lu- ja, al- le- lu- ja, al- le- lu- ja.
-ja, al- le- lu- ja, al- le- lu- ja.
-ja, al- le- lu- ja, al- le- lu- ja.

27. Regina caeli (2)

18
- - re, quem me- ru- i- sti por- ta-
Qui- a quem me- ru- i- sti por- ta-
-sti por- ta- re, quem me- ru- i- sti por- ta-
Qui- a quem me- ru- i- sti por- ta-
23
-re, al- le- lu- ja, al- le- lu- - ja, al- le- lu- ja,
-re, al- le- lu- ja, al- le- lu- ja, al- le- lu- ja,
-re, al- le- lu- - ja, al- le- lu- ja,
-re, al- le- lu- ja, al- le- lu- ja, al- le-
28
al- le- lu- ja, al- le- lu- ja: Re- sur- re- xit, sic-
al- le- lu- ja, al- le- lu- ja: sic- ut
al- le- lu- ja, al- le- lu- ja: Re- sur- re- xit, sic- ut
-lu- ja, al- le- lu- ja: Re- sur- re- xit, sic- ut

33
-ut di- xit, al- le- lu- ja, al- le- lu- ja, al- le- lu- ja: O-
di- xit, al- - le- lu- ja, al- le- lu- ja, al- le- lu- ja: O-
di- xit, al- - le- lu- ja, al- le- lu- ja, al- le- lu- ja:
di- xit, al- - le- lu- ja, al- le- lu- ja, al- le- lu- ja:
39
-ra pro no- - bis, De- um, al- le- lu-
-ra pro no- bis, De- - um, al- le- lu-
al- le- lu-
al- le- lu-
45
-ja, al- le- lu- ja, al- le- lu- ja, al- le- lu- ja, al- le- lu- ja.
-ja, al- le- lu- ja, al- le- lu- ja, al- le- lu- ja, al- le- lu- ja.
-ja, al- le- lu- ja, al- le- lu- ja, al- le- lu- ja, al- le- lu- ja.
-ja, al- le- lu- ja, al- le- lu- ja, al- le- lu- ja, al- le- lu- ja.

28. Regina caeli (3)

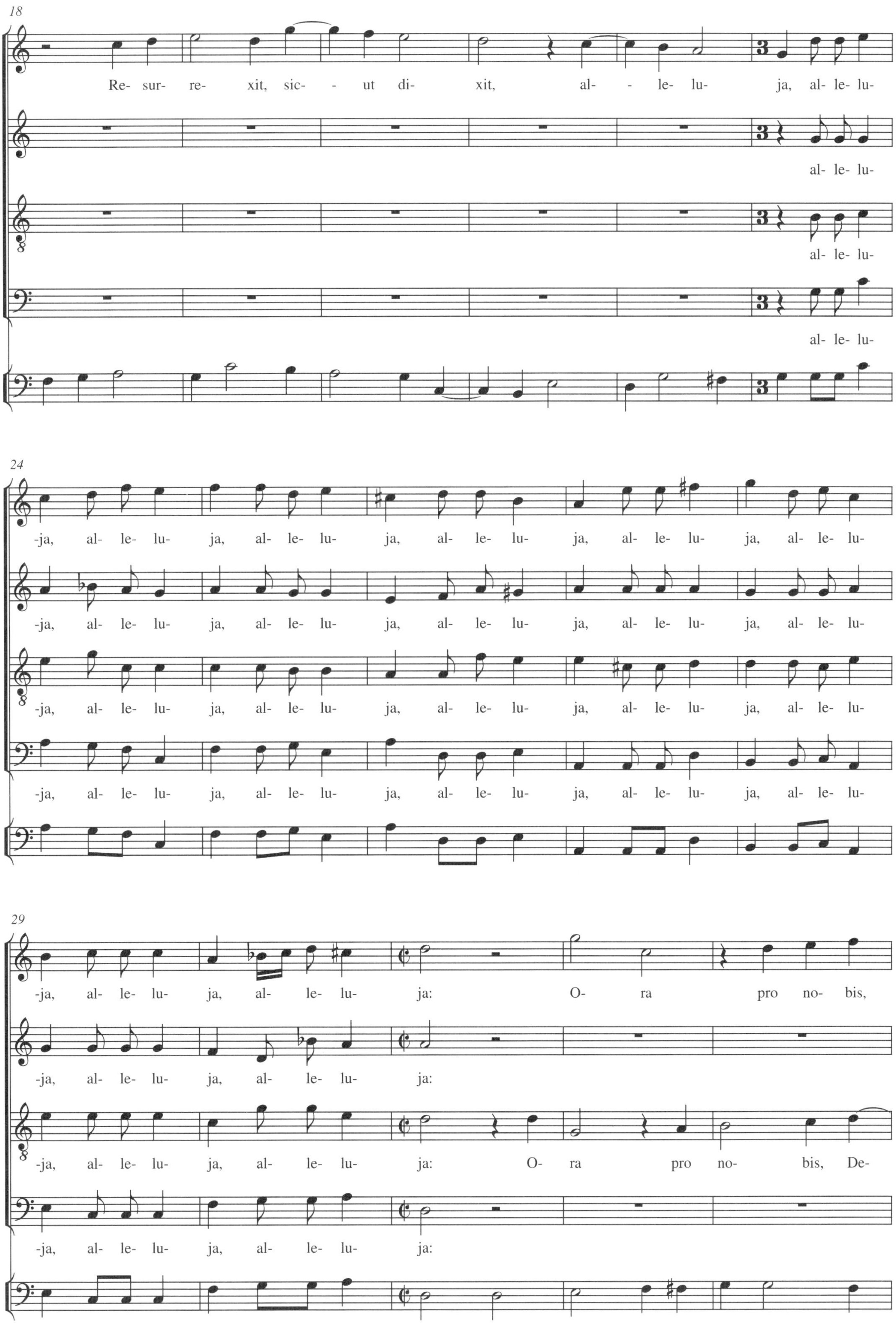

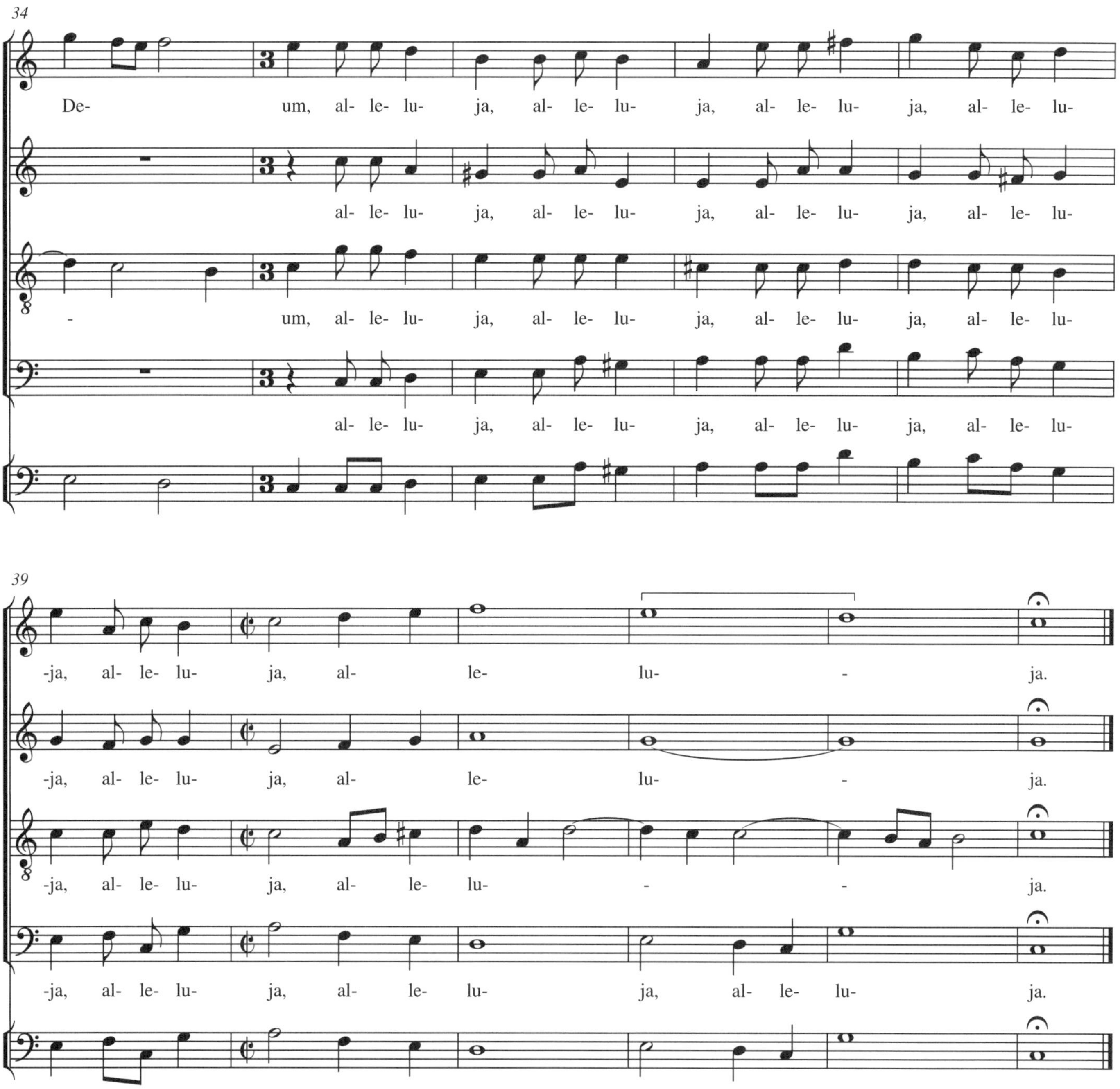

29. Regnum mundi

16
-di, quem di- le- xi, al- le- lu- ja. E- ru- cta-
-di, quem di- le- xi, al- le- lu- ja.
-di, quem di- le- - xi, al- le- lu- ja.
-di, quem di- le- xi, al- le- lu- ja.
21
-vit cor me- um ver- bum bo- num, di- co e- go o- pe- ra, o- pe-
di- co e- go o- - pe- ra, o- pe-
di- co e- go o- pe- ra
di- co e- go o- pe- ra, o- pe-
26
-ra me- - a, o- pe- ra me- - a re- gi. Quem
-ra me- a re- gi, o- pe- ra me- a re- gi. Quem vi-
me- a re- gi, o- pe- ra me- a re- gi.
-ra me- a re- gi, o- pe- ra me- a re- gi.

vi- di, quem a- ma- vi, in quem cre- di- di, quem di- le- xi,
- di, quem vi- di, quem a- ma- vi, in quem cre- di- di, quem di- le- xi,
in quem cre- di- di, quem di- le- - xi,
in quem cre- di- di, quem di- le- xi,
al- le- lu- ja. Glo- ri- a Pa- tri, et Fi- li- o,
al- le- lu- ja.
al- le- lu- ja. et
al- le- lu- ja. et
et Spi- ri- tu- i San- cto. Re- gnum mun- di et om- nem or-
et Spi- ri- tu- i San- cto.
Spi- ri- tu- i San- cto.
Spi- ri- tu- i San- cto.

47
-na- tum sae- - cu- li con- tem- psi, pro- pter a- mo- rem Do- mi- ni me-
pro- pter a- mo- rem Do- mi- ni me-
pro- pter a mo- rem Do- mi- ni me-
pro- pter a- mo- rem Do- mi- ni me- i,
53
- i, Je- - su Chri- sti. Quem vi- di, quem a- ma-
-i, Je- su, Je- su Chri- sti. Quem vi- - di, quem vi- di, quem a- ma-
-i, Je- su, Je- su Chri- sti. in
Je- su, Je- su Chri- sti. in
58
-vi, in quem cre- di- di, quem di- le- xi, al- le- lu- ja.
-vi, in quem cre- di- di, quem di- le- xi, al- le- lu- ja.
quem cre- di- di, quem di- le- - xi, al- le- lu- ja.
quem cre- di- di, quem di- le- xi, al- le- lu- ja.

30. Salve Regina (1)

15
Ad te su- - spi- ra- mus, ge- men-
Ad te su- - spi- ra- mus, ge- men-
te, ad te su- - spi- ra- mus, ge- men-
Ad te su- - spi- ra- mus, ge- men-
22
-tes et flen- - tes in hac la-
-tes et flen- tes, et flen- tes in hac la- cri-
-tes et flen- - - tes in hac la- cri-
-tes et flen- - tes in hac la- cri-
28
-cri- ma- rum val- - le. E- - ja, e-
-ma- rum val- - le.
-ma- rum val- le, val- le.
-ma- rum val- le.

35
- ja er- go, Ad- vo- ca- ta no- stra, il- - los tu-
Ad- vo- ca- - ta no- stra, il- los tu-
Ad- vo- ca- ta no- stra, il- los tu-
Ad- vo- ca- ta no- stra, il- - los tu-
41
-os mi- - se- ri- cor- des o- cu- los ad nos con-
-os mi- se- ri- cor- des o- cu- los ad nos con- ver- te, con-
-os mi- se- ri- cor- des o- cu- los ad nos con- ver-
-os mi- se- ri- cor- des o- cu- los ad nos con- ver-
46
-ver- te. Et Je- sum, be- - ne-
-ver- te. Et Je- sum, be- ne- di-
- te. Et Je- sum, be- - ne-
- te. Et Je- - sum, be-

53
-di- - ctum fru- ctum ven- tris tu-
- - ctum fru- ctum ven- tris tu-
-di- - ctum fru- - ctum ven- - tris tu-
-ne- di- ctum fru- ctum ven- tris
60
-i, no- bis post hoc ex- - si- - li-
-i, no- bis post hoc ex- si- li- um o- sten-
- i, no- - bis post hoc ex-
tu- i, no- bis post hoc ex- si- li- um o-
66
-um o- - sten- - de. O
-de, ex- si- li- um o- sten- de.
-si- li- um o- sten- de. O
-sten- - - de.

72
clemens, o clemens: O
O clemens, o clemens:
clemens, o cle- - mens: O
O clemens, o clemens:
79
pia, o pia: O
O pi- - - a: O
pia, o pi- - a:
O pi- a: O dul-
85
dul- - cis Vir- go, Vir- - go Ma- ri- a.
dul- - - cis Vir- - go Ma- ri- a.
O dul- cis Vir- go Ma- ri- a, Ma- ri- - a.
-cis Vir- go Ma- ri- a, Ma- ri- - a.

31. Salve Regina (2)

16
-les, fi- li- i E- - vae. Ad
-les, fi- - li- i E- - vae. Ad
- su- les, fi- li- i E- vae.
-les, fi- li- i E- - vae.
23
te su- - spi- ra- mus, ge- men- tes et
te su- spi- ra- - mus, ge- men- tes et
ge- men- tes et
ge- men- tes et
30
flen- tes in hac la- cri- ma- - -
flen- tes in hac la- - cri- ma-
flen- tes in hac la- cri- ma- - rum
flen- tes in hac la- cri- ma- - rum

37
-rum val- le. E- - ja
- rum val- le. E- - ja er- go,
val- - le.
val- - le.
45
er- go, Ad- vo- ca- ta no- stra,
Ad- vo- ca- - ta no- - stra,
51
il- los tu- os mi- se- ri- cor- des o- cu- los ad
il- los tu- os mi- se- ri- cor- des o- cu- los ad
il- los tu- os mi- se- ri- cor- des o- cu- los ad
il- los tu- os mi- se- ri- cor- des o- cu- los ad

58
nos con- ver- te. Et Je-
nos con- ver- te. Et Je- sum, et
nos con- ver- te.
nos con- ver- te.
65
-sum, be- - ne- di- ctum fru- ctum ven- -
Je- sum, be- ne- di- - ctum fru- - ctum ven- -
72
- tris tu- i, no- bis post hoc ex- si- li-
-tris tu- - i, no- bis post hoc ex- si- li-
no- bis post hoc ex- si- li-
no- bis post hoc ex- si- li-

79
-um o- sten- de. O
-um o- - sten- de. O
-um o- sten- de.
-um o- sten- de.
85
cle- mens: O pi- - a:
cle- mens: O pi- - a: O
O pi- a: O
O pi- - a: O
92
O dul- cis Vir- go Ma- ri- a.
dul- cis Vir- - go Ma- ri- a.
dul- cis Vir- - go Ma- ri- - a.
dul- cis Vir- - go Ma- ri- a.

32. Salve Regina (3)

24
fi- li- i E- vae. Ad
fi- li- i E- - - vae.
fi- li- i E- - vae. Ad te
fi- li- i E- vae.
31
te su- spi- ra- mus, ge- men- tes et flen-
ge- men- tes et flen-
su- spi- ra- mus, su- - spi- ra- mus, ge- men- tes et flen-
ge- men- tes et flen-
38
-tes in hac la- - cri- ma- - rum val-
-tes in hac la- - cri- ma- rum
-tes in hac la- cri- ma- - rum val-
-tes in hac la- - cri- ma- - rum val-

45
- le. E- - ja er-
val- le.
- le. E- - ja er- go, Ad- vo- ca-
- le.
52
-go, Ad- vo- ca- ta no- stra, il- los tu- os mi-
il- los tu- os
- ta no- - stra, il- - los tu- -
il- - los tu- os
59
-se- ri- cor- - - des o- cu- los ad nos con- ver-
mi- se- ri- cor- - des o- cu- los ad nos con-
-os mi- se- ri- cor- - des o- cu- los ad nos con-
mi- se- ri- cor- des o- cu- los ad nos con-

66
- te. Et Je- - sum, be- ne- di- ctum
-ver- - te. Et Je-
-ver- - te.
-ver- te.
73
fru- - ctum, fru- - ctum ven- tris tu- i,
- sum, be- ne- di- - ctum fru- ctum ven- tris tu- i,
80
no- bis post hoc ex- si- li- um o- sten- -
no- bis post hoc ex- si- li- um o- - sten- -
no- bis post hoc ex- si- li- um o- sten- -
no- bis post hoc ex- si- li- um o- sten- -

87
-de. O clemens: O pi-
-de. O pi- -
-de.
-de.
94
-a, o cle- mens: o pi-
-a, o cle- mens: o pi- - -
100
-a: O dul- cis Vir- go Ma- - ri- - a.
-a: O dul- cis Vir- go Ma- ri- - a.
O dul- cis Vir- go Ma- ri- - a.
O dul- cis Vir- go Ma- ri- - a.

33. Sancta Maria

16
-les: o- ra, o- ra pro po- pu- lo, in- ter- ve- ni pro cle-
-les: o- ra, o- ra pro po- pu- lo, in- ter- ve- ni pro cle-
-les:
-les:
21
-ro, in- ter- ve- ni pro cle- ro, in- ter- ce- de, in- ter- ce- de pro de- vo-
-ro, in- ter- ve- ni pro cle- ro, in- ter- ce- - de pro de- vo-
in- ter- ve- ni pro cle- ro, in- ter- ce- de pro de- vo-
in- ter- ve- ni pro cle- ro, in- ter- ce- de pro de- vo-
26
-to fe- mi- ne- o se- xu, fe- mi- ne- o se- xu:
-to fe- mi- ne- o se- xu, fe- mi- ne- o se- xu: sen- ti-
-to fe- mi- ne- o se- xu, fe- mi- ne- o se- xu:
-to fe- mi- ne- o se- xu, fe- mi- ne- o se- xu:

31
sen- ti- ant om- nes tu- um ju- va- men, qui- cum- que ce- le-
-ant om- nes, sen- ti- ant om- nes tu- um ju- va- men, qui- cum- - que ce- le-
qui- cum- que ce- le-
qui- cum- que ce- le-
37
-brant tu- am san- ctam com- me- mo- ra- ti- o- nem, com- me- mo- ra- ti-
-brant tu- am san- ctam com- me- - mo- ra- ti- o- nem, com-
-brant tu- am san- ctam com- me- mo- ra- ti- o- nem, com- me- mo- ra- ti-
-brant tu- am san- ctam com- me- mo- ra- ti- o- nem, com- me- mo- ra-
42
-o- nem, com- me- mo- ra- ti- o- nem. Al- le- lu- ja.
-me- mo- ra- ti- o- nem, com- me- mo- ra- ti- o- nem. Al- le- lu- ja.
-o- nem, com- me- mo- ra- - ti- o- nem. Al- le- lu- ja.
- ti- o- nem, com- me- mo- ra- ti- o- nem. Al- le- lu- ja.

34. Tu es Petrus

10
-am me- am, ae- di- fi- ca- bo,
ae- di- fi- ca- bo Ec- cle- si- am me- am, ae- di- fi-
ae- di- fi- ca- bo Ec- cle- si- am me- am, ae- di- fi-
ae- di- fi- ca- bo Ec- cle- si- am me- am, ae- di- fi- ca-
ae- di- fi- ca- bo Ec- cle- si- am me- am, ae- di- fi-
14
ae- di- fi- ca- - bo Ec- cle- si-
-ca- bo Ec- cle- si- am me- am,
-ca- bo, ae- di- fi- ca- bo Ec- cle- si- am me- am,
-bo Ec- cle- si- am me- am,
-ca- bo Ec- cle- si- am me- am,

18
-am, Ec- cle- si- am me- am:
ae- di- fi- ca- bo Ec- cle- si- am me-
ae- di- fi- ca- - bo Ec- cle- si- am me-
ae- di- fi- ca- bo Ec- cle- si- am me-
ae- di- fi- ca- bo Ec- cle- si- am me-

22
et por- tas in- fer- ni non prae- va- le- bunt ad- ver- sus e- am,
-am: et por- tas in- fer- ni, et
-am: et por- tas in- fer- ni, et
-am: et por- tas in- fer- ni,
-am: et

27
ad- ver- sus
por- tas in- fer- ni non prae- va- le- bunt ad- ver- - sus e- am.
por- tas in- fer- ni non prae- va- le- bunt ad- ver- sus e- am, ad-
in- fer- ni non prae-va- le- bunt ad-ver- sus e- am, ad-
por- tas in- fer- ni non prae- va- le- bunt ad- ver- sus e- am, ad- ver-
32
e- am. A- - - men.
A- - - - men
-ver- sus e- am. A- - - men.
-ver- sus e- am. A- - men.
- sus e- am. A- - - men.

35. Tu es vas electionis

10
-le, San- cte Pau- - le A- po- sto-
Sancte Paule Apostole,
San- cte Pau- - le, Pau- le A- po- sto- le,
San- cte Pau- le A- po- sto- le,
San- cte Pau- le A- po- sto- le,
[♭]
15
-le, prae- di- ca- tor ve- ri- ta-
San- cte Pau- le, Pau- - le A- po- sto- le, prae- di-
San- cte Pau- le, Pau- le A- po- sto- le,
San- cte Pau- le, Pau- le A- po- sto- le,
San- cte Pau- le, Pau- le A- po- sto- le,

20
-tis et do- ctor, et do- ctor gen- ti- um,
ca- tor, prae- di- ca- tor ve- ri- ta- tis et
prae- di- ca- - tor ve- ri- ta- tis et
prae- di- ca- tor ve- ri- ta- tis
prae- di- ca- tor ve- ri- ta- - tis et
25
et do- ctor, et do- ctor gen- ti-
do- ctor, et do- ctor gen- ti- um, et
do- ctor, et do- ctor gen- ti- um,
et do- ctor gen- ti- um, et
do- ctor, et do- ctor gen- ti- um, et

30
-um, per quem om- nes gen- tes co-gno- ve- runt gra- ti- am
do- ctor gen- ti- um,
et do- ctor gen- ti- um, gen- ti- um,
do- ctor gen- ti- um,
do- ctor gen- ti- um,
35
De- i.
per quem om- nes gen- tes co- gno- ve- runt gra- - ti- am
per quem om- nes gen- tes co-gno- ve- runt gra- ti- am
per quem om- nes gen- tes co- gno- ve- runt gra- ti- am
per quem om- nes gen- tes co-gno- ve- runt gra- - ti- am

40
In- - ter- ce- de pro no- bis, in- ter- ce- de pro no-
De- i. In- - ter- ce- de pro no- bis,
De- i. In- ter-
De- i. In- ter-
De- i. In- ter-
45
-bis ad De- um qui te e- le- git,
in- ter- ce- de pro no- bis ad De- um qui
-ce- de pro no- bis ad De- um qui
-ce- de pro no- bis ad De- um qui
-ce- de pro no- bis ad De- um qui

50
ad De- um
te e- le- git, ad De- um, ad De- - um qui te e- le-
te e- le- git, ad De- um, ad De- um, ad De- um
te e- le- git, ad De- um, ad De- um qui te
te e- le- git, ad De- um, ad De- um, ad De- um qui
55
qui te e- le- git. Al- le- lu- ja, al- le- lu- - ja, al- le- lu-
-git, qui te e- le- git. Al- lc- lu- ja, al- le- lu-
qui te e- le- git. Al- le- lu- ja, al- le- lu-
e- le- git, e- le- git. Al- le- lu- ja, al- le- lu- ja, al- le- lute e- le- git, e- le- git. Al- le- lu- ja, al- le- lu-

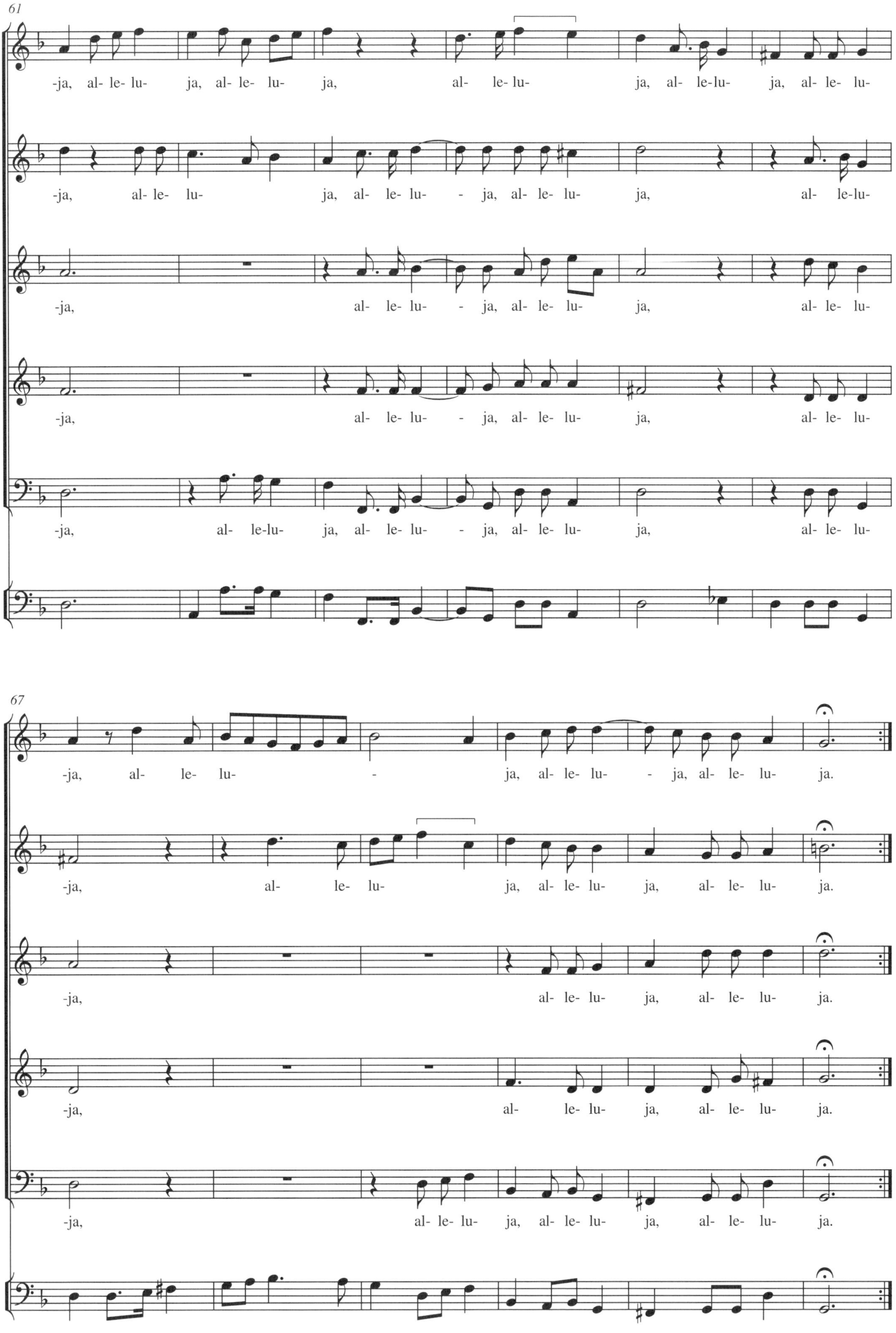

36. Veni Sancte Spiritus

16
-de. Qui per di- ver- si- ta- tem, di- ver- si- ta- tem cun- cta- rum lin- gua-
-de. Qui per di- ver- si- ta- tem cun- cta- rum lin-
-de.
-de.
21
-rum, lin- gua- rum gen- tes in u- ni- ta- te fi- de-
-gua- rum gen- tes in u- ni- ta- te fi- de-
gen- tes in u- ni- ta- te fi- de-
gen- tes in u- ni- ta- te fi- de-
26
-i con- gre- ga- sti. Al- le- lu- ja, al- le- lu- ja, al- le- lu-
-i con- gre- ga- sti. Al- le- lu- ja, al- le- lu- ja, al- le- lu-
-i con- gre- ga- sti.
-i con- gre- ga- sti. Al- le- lu- ja,

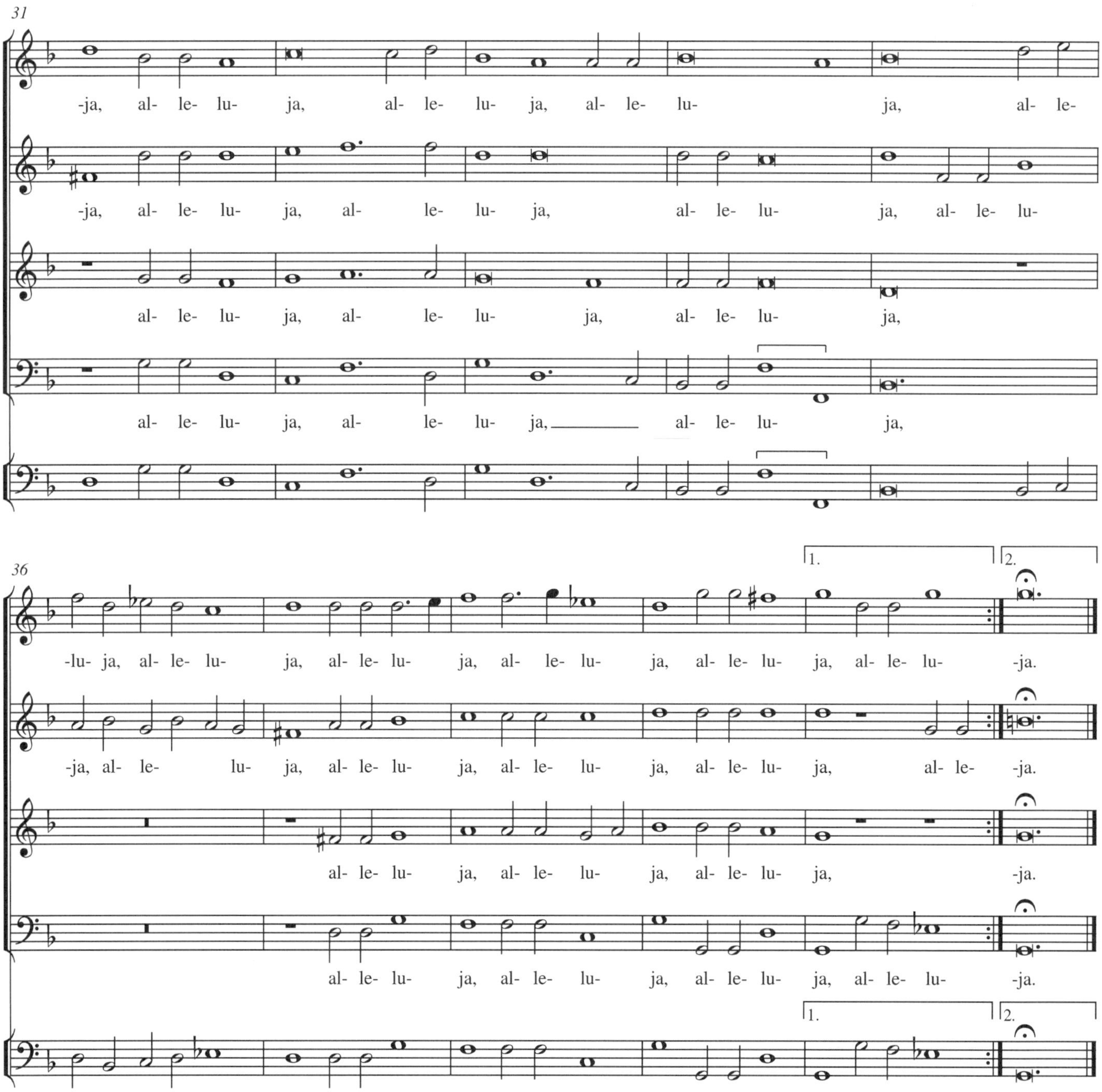

37. Vir Domini Benedictus

Vir Domini Benedictus, vir Domini Benedictus, vir Domini Benedictus omnium justorum spiritu plenus fuit: ipse inter-

14
-ce- dat, in- ter- ce- dat pro cun- ctis mo- na- sti- cae pro-
in- ter- ce- dat pro cun- ctis mo- na- sti- cae
in- ter- ce- dat pro cun- ctis mo- na- sti- cae pro-
in- ter- ce- dat pro cun- ctis mo- na- sti- cae pro-
18
-fes- si- o- nis, i- pse in- ter- ce- dat pro cun-
pro- fes- si- o- nis, i- pse in- ter- ce- dat pro cun-
-fes- si- o- nis, pro cun-
-fes- si- o- nis, i- pse in- ter- ce- dat pro cun-
22
-ctis mo- na- - sti- cae pro- fes- si- o- nis. Al- le- lu-
-ctis mo- na- - sti- cae pro- fes- si- o- nis.
-ctis mo- na- - sti- cae pro- - fes- si- o- nis.
-ctis mo- na- - sti- cae pro- fes- si- o- nis.

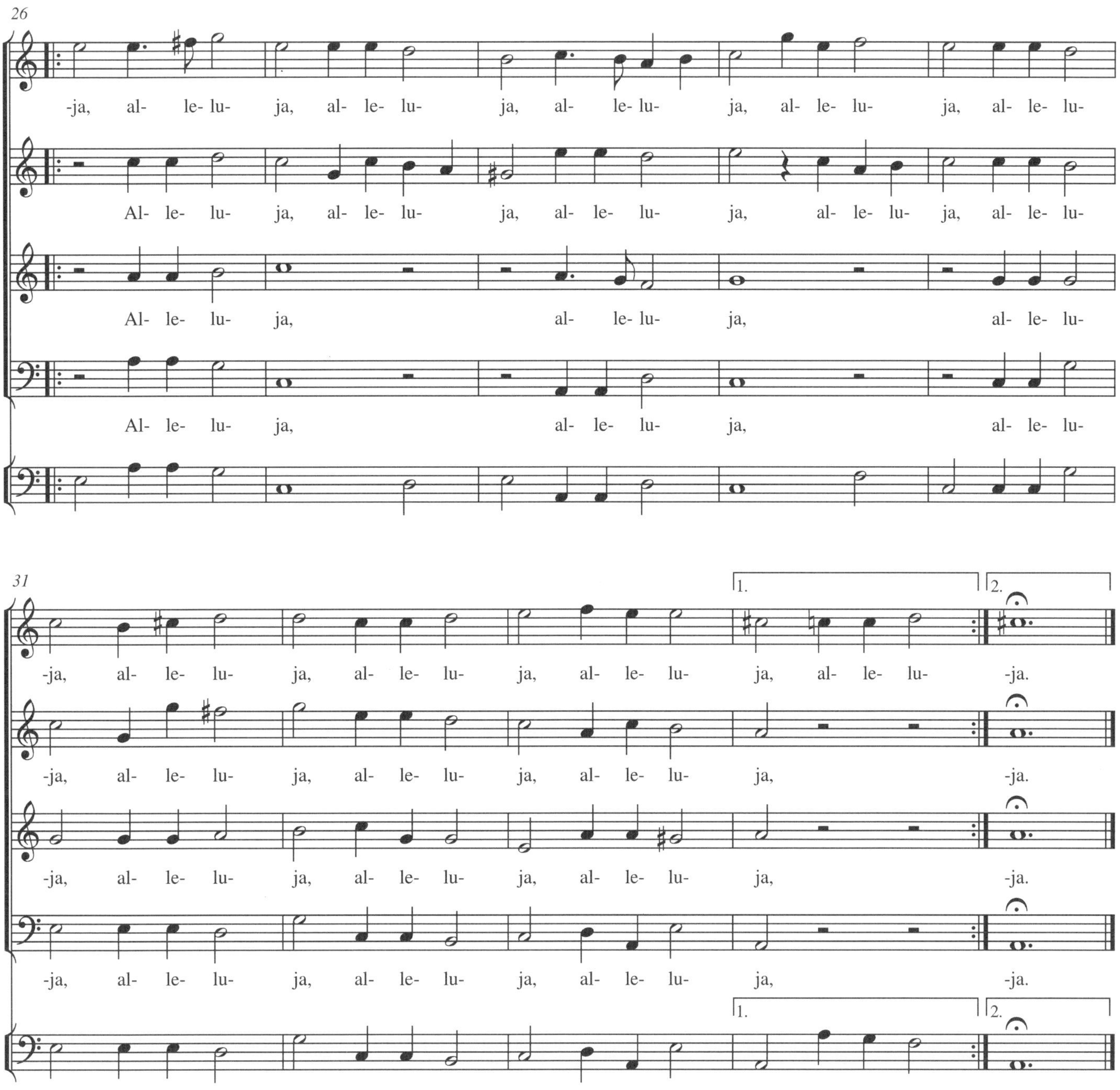

Hymns

38. Ad caenam Agni

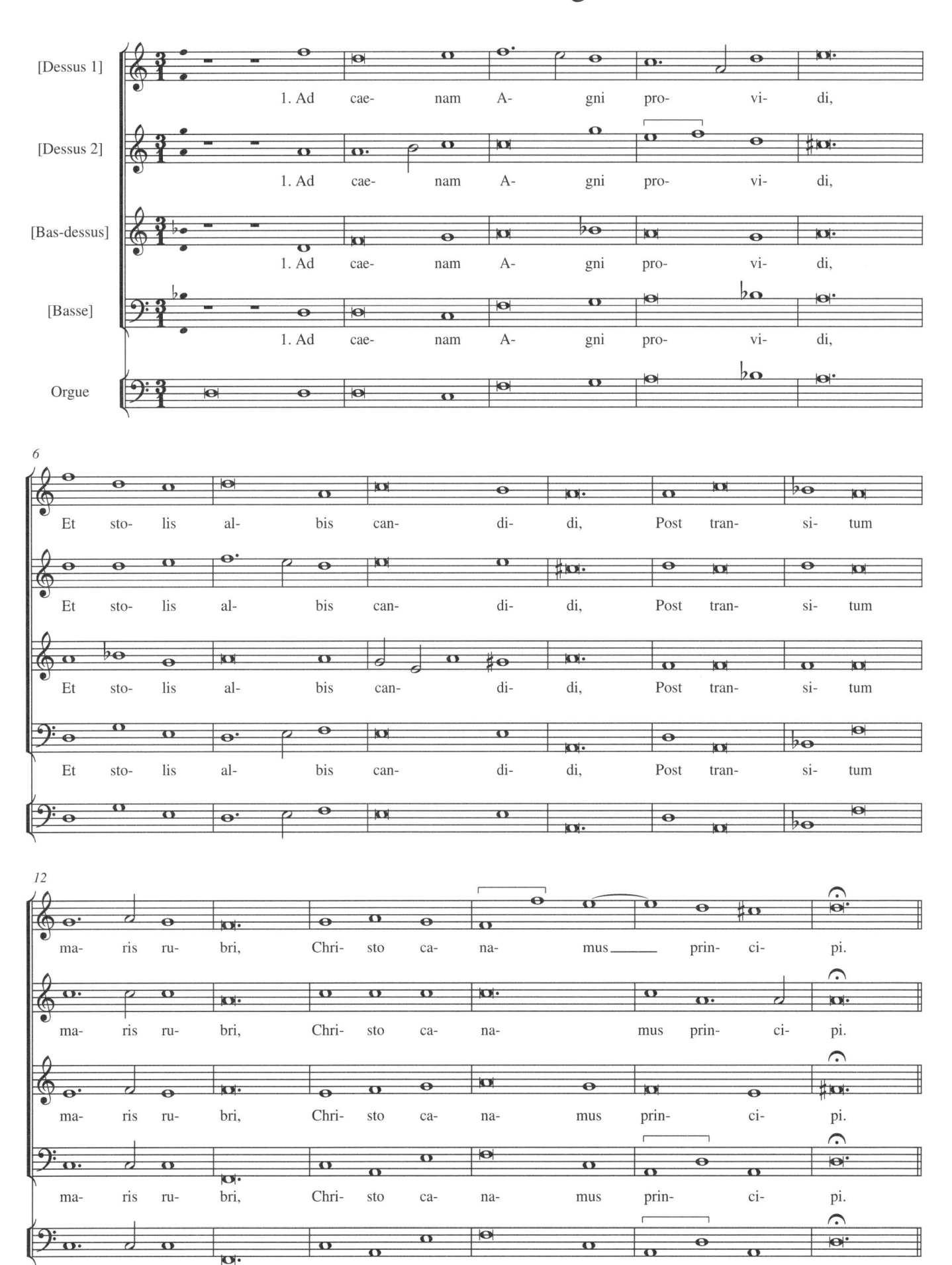

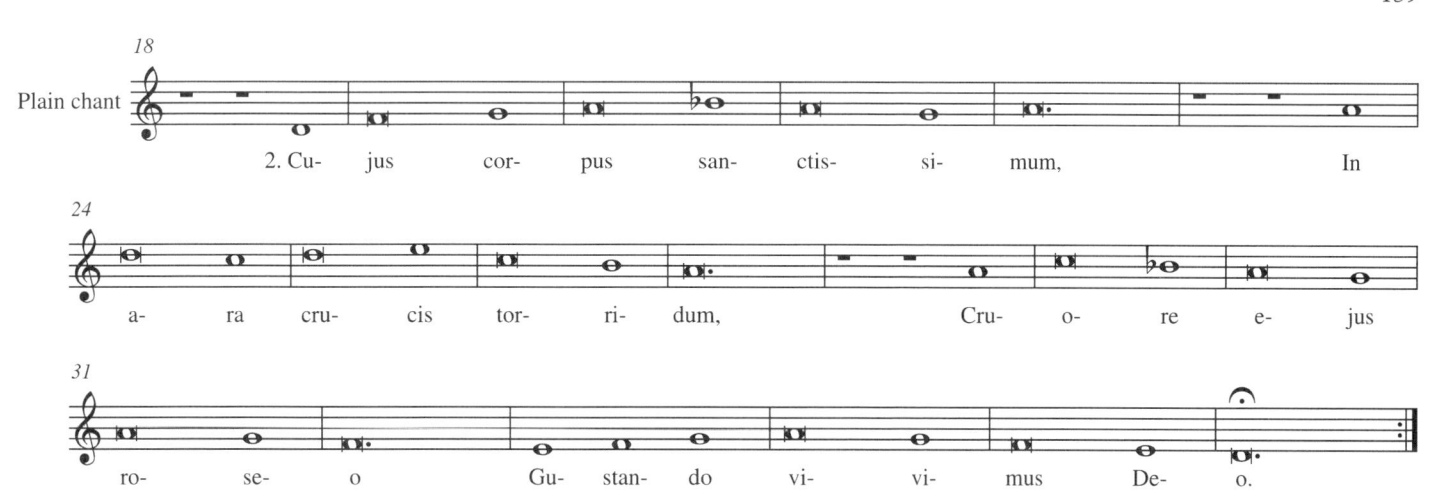

2. Cujus corpus sanctissimum,
In ara crucis torridum,
Cruore ejus roseo
Gustando vivimus Deo.

3. Protecti Paschae vespero
   A devastante Angelo,
   Erepti de durissimo
   Pharaonis imperio.

4. Jam Pascha nostrum Christus est,
   Qui immolatus Agnus est,
   Sinceritatis azyma,
   Caro ejus oblata est.

5. O vere digna hostia,
   Per quam fracta sunt tartara,
   Redempta plebs captivita,
   Reddita vitae praemia.

6. Consurgit Christus tumulo,
   Victor redit de barathro,
   Tyrannum trudens vinculo,
   Et Paradisum reserans.

7. Quaesumus, Auctor omnium,
   In hoc paschali gaudio,
   Ab omni mortis impetu
   Tuum defende populum.

8. Gloria tibi Domine,
   Qui surrexisti a mortuis,
   Cum Patre et Sancto Spiritu,
   In sempiterna saecula.

39. Alleluja. O filii et filiae

6
o. = o
Al- le- lu- ja, al- le- lu- ja, al- le-
Al- le- lu- ja, al- le- lu- ja, al- - le-
-le- lu- ja, al- le- lu- ja, al- le- lu- ja, al- le-
Al- le- lu- ja, al- le- lu- ja, al- le-
Al- le- lu- ja, al- le- lu- ja, al- le-
13
o = o.
-lu- ja. 1. O fi- li- i et fi- li- ae, Rex
-lu- ja. 1. O fi li i ct fi- li- ae, Rex
-lu- ja. 1. O fi- li- i et fi- li- ae, Rex
-lu- ja.
-lu- ja. 1. O fi- li- i et fi- li- ae, Rex

20
cae- le- stis, Rex glo- ri- ae, Mor- te sur- re- xit ho- di-
cae- le- stis, Rex glo- ri- ae, Mor- te sur- re- xit ho- di-
cae- le- stis, Rex glo- ri- ae,
cae- le- stis, Rex glo- ri- ae,
27
-e. Al- le- lu- ja. Al- le- lu- ja, al- le- lu- ja, al-
-e. Al- le- lu- ja. Al- le- lu- ja, al- le- lu- ja, al-
Al- le- lu- ja, al- le- lu- ja, al-
Al- le- lu- ja, al- le- lu- ja, al-
Al- le- lu- ja, al- le- lu- ja, al-

34
-le- lu- ja, al- le- lu- ja, al- le- lu- ja, al- le- lu- ja, al-
-le- lu- ja, al-
-le- lu- ja,
-le- lu- ja, al-
-le- lu- ja, al-
42
-le- lu- ja, al- le- lu- ja, al- le- lu- ja.
-le- lu- ja, al- le- lu- ja, al- - le- lu- ja.
al- le- lu- ja, al- le- lu- ja, al- le- lu- ja.
-le- lu- ja, al- le- lu- ja, al- le- lu- ja.
-le- lu- ja, al- le- lu- ja, al- le- lu- ja.

2. Et mane prima sabathi, Ad ostium monumenti, Accesserunt discipuli. Alleluja.

164

79
-ma, vi- de la- tus, Vi- de pe- des, vi- de ma- nus,
-ma, vi- de la- tus, Vi- de pe- des, vi- de ma- nus,
-ma, vi- de la- tus, Vi- de pe- des, vi- de ma- nus, No- li es-
-ma, vi- de la- tus, Vi- de pe- des, vi- de ma- nus,
87
Al- le- lu- ja, al- le- lu-
Al- le- lu- ja, al- le- lu-
-se in- cre- du- lus. Al- le- lu- ja. Al- le- lu- ja, al- le- lu-
Al- le- lu- ja, al- le- lu-

95
-ja, al- le- lu- ja, al- le- lu- ja, al- le- lu- ja, al- le- lu-
-ja, al- le- lu- ja,
-ja, al- le- lu- ja,
-ja, al- le- lu- ja,
103
-ja, al- le- lu- ja, al- le- lu- ja, al- le- lu- ja.
al- le- lu- ja, al- le- lu- ja, al- - le- lu- ja.
al- le- lu- ja, al- le- lu- ja, al- le- lu- ja.
al- le- lu- ja, al- le- lu- ja, al- le- lu- ja.
al- le- lu- ja, al- le- lu- ja, al- le- lu- ja.

40. Aurea luce

1. Aurea luce et decore roseo, Lux lucis omne perfudisti saeculum, Decorans caelos inclito martyrio,

Hac sacra die, quae dat reis veniam.

Plain chant: 2. Janitor caeli, Doctor orbis pariter, Judices saecli, vera mundi lumina: Per crucem alter, alter ense triumphans, Vitae senatum laureati possident.

3. O felix Roma quae tantorum principum,

50
Es pur- pu- ra- ta pre- ti- o- - sa san- gui-
Es pur- pu- ra- ta pre- ti- o- sa san- gui-
Es pur- pu- ra- ta pre- ti- o- sa san- gui-
Es pur- pu- ra- ta pre- ti- o- sa san- gui-
55
-ne, Non lau- de tu- a, non lau- de tu- a sed i- pso-
-ne, Non lau- de tu- a, non lau- de tu- a sed i- pso-
-ne, Non lau- de tu- a
-ne, Non lau- de tu- a
61
-rum me- ri- tis, sed i- pso- rum me- ri- tis,
-rum me- ri- tis, sed i- pso- rum me- ri- tis,
sed i- pso- rum me- - ri- tis,
sed i- pso- rum me- - ri- tis,

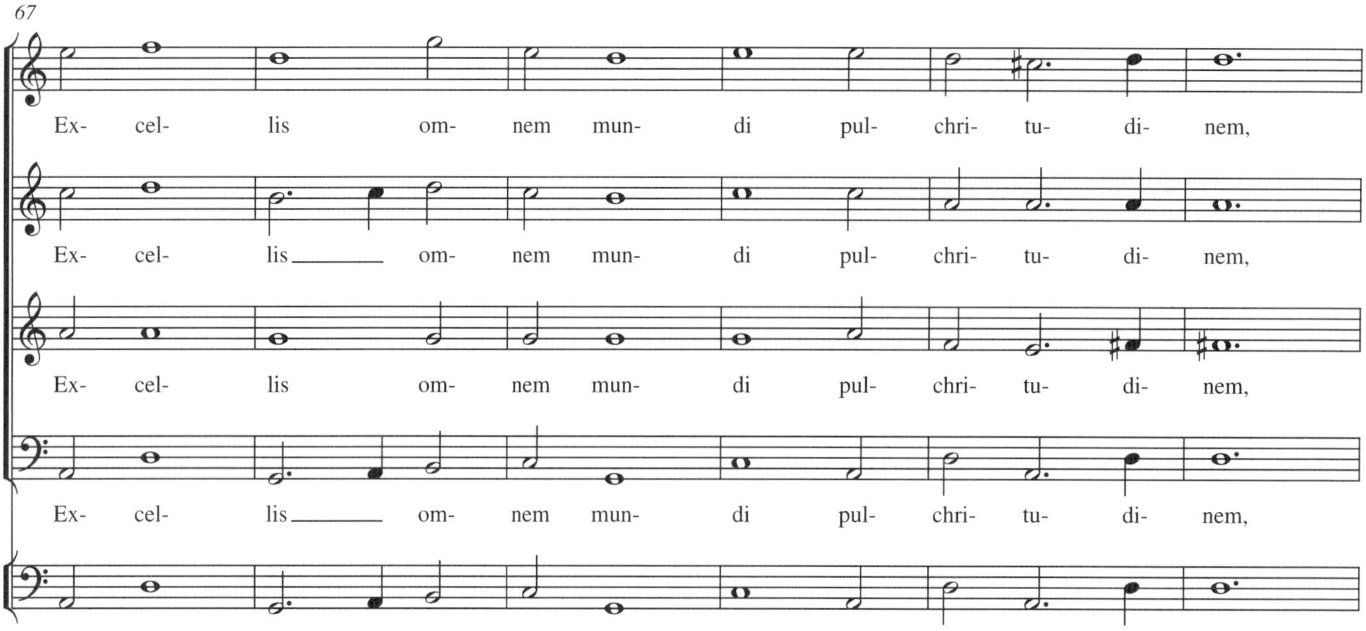
67
Ex- cel- lis om- nem mun- di pul- chri- tu- di- nem,
Ex- cel- lis om- nem mun- di pul- chri- tu- di- nem,
Ex- cel- lis om- nem mun- di pul- chri- tu- di- nem,
Ex- cel- lis om- nem mun- di pul- chri- tu- di- nem,

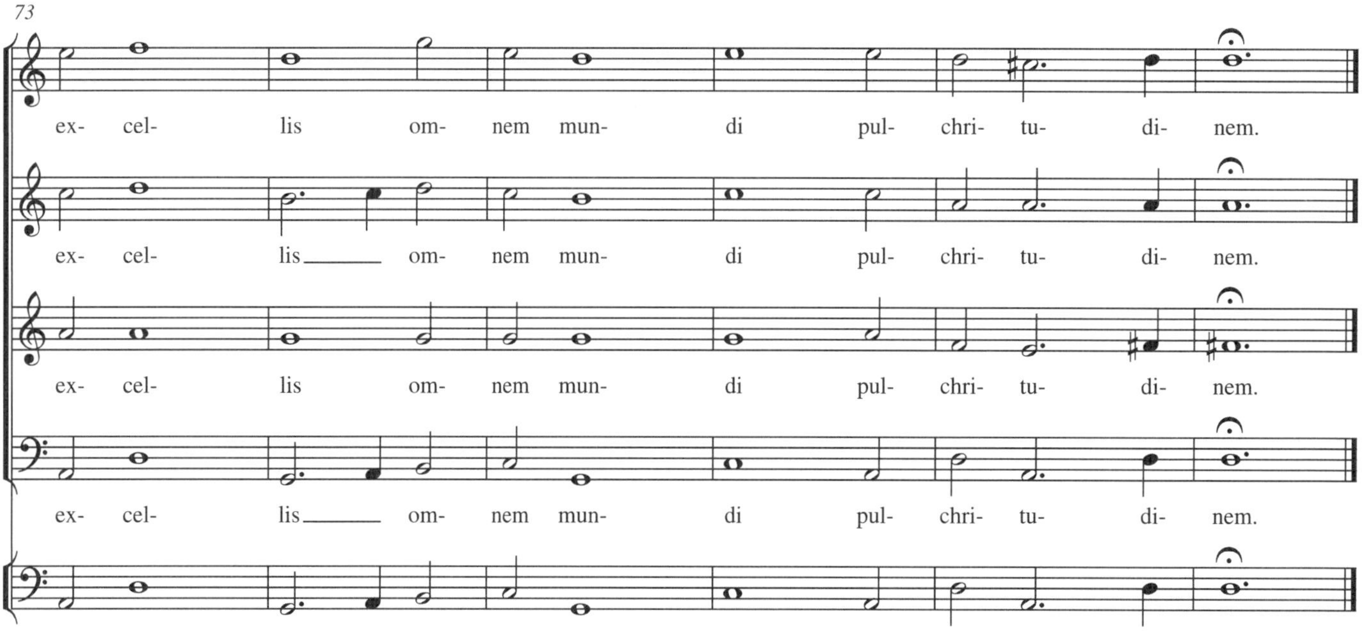
73
ex- cel- lis om- nem mun- di pul- chri- tu- di- nem.
ex- cel- lis om- nem mun- di pul- chri- tu- di- nem.
ex- cel- lis om- nem mun- di pul- chri- tu- di- nem.
ex- cel- lis om- nem mun- di pul- chri- tu- di- nem.

41. Ave maris stella

172

Plain chant: 2. Sumens illud Ave Gabrielis ore, Funda nos in pace, Mutans Evae nomen.

3. Solve vincla reis, Profer lumen caecis: Mala nostra pelle, Bona cuncta posce.

Plain chant: 4. Monstra te esse matrem: Sumat per te preces, Qui pro nobis natus, Tulit esse tuus.

5. Virgo singularis, Inter omnes mitis, Nos culpis solutos, Mites fac et castos.

6. Vitam praesta puram Iter para tutum: Ut videntes Jesum, Semper collaetemur.

7. Sit laus Deo Patri, Summo Christo decus, Spiritui Sancto, Tribus honor unus. Amen.

42. Ave mater pia

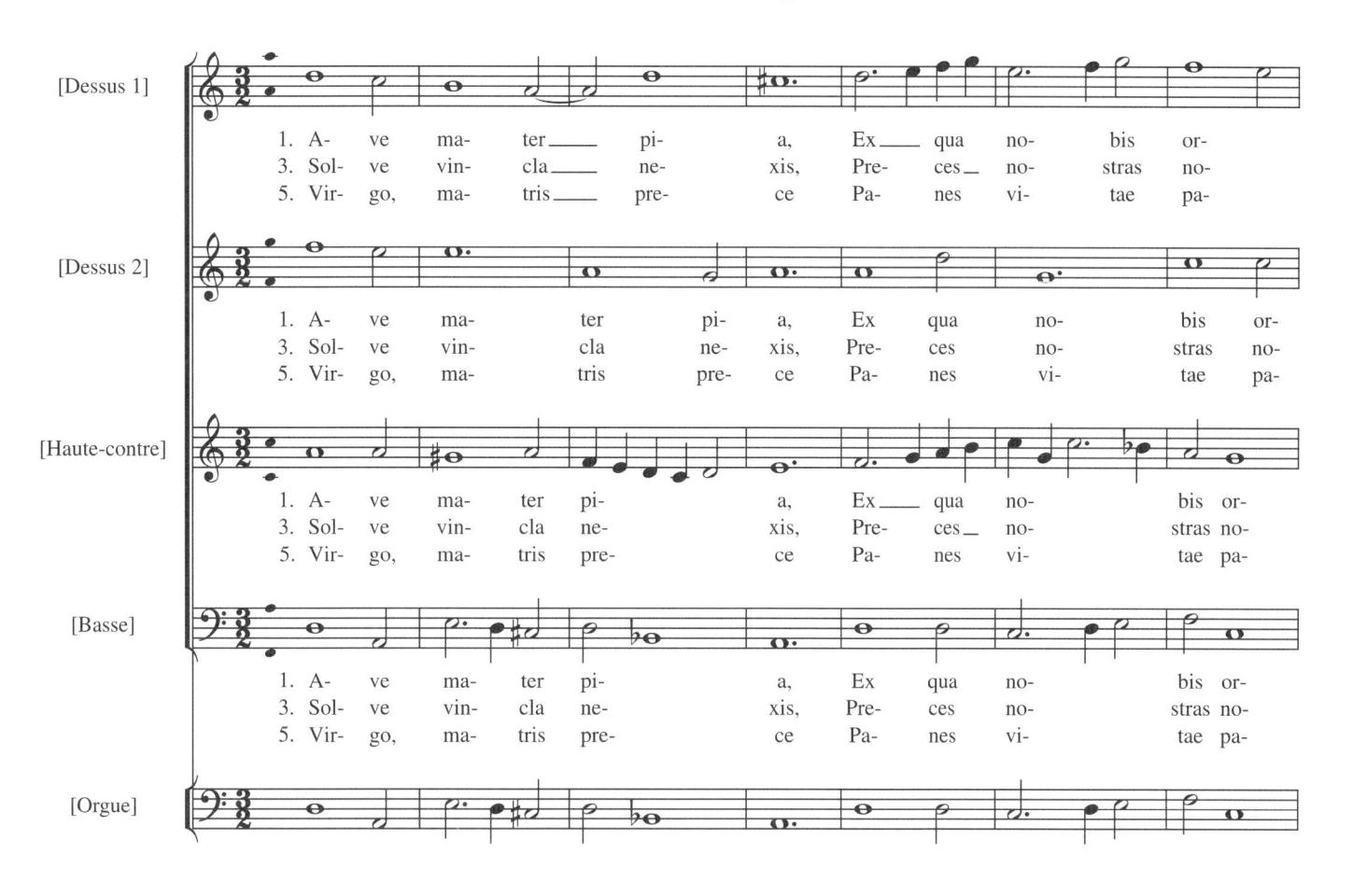

1. A- ve ma- ter pi- a, Ex qua no- bis or-ta Est Virgo Maria, Felix caeli porta.
3. Sol- ve vin- cla ne- xis, Preces nostras nosce, Sordes lava fessis, Bona cuncta posce.
5. Vir- go, ma- tris pre- ce Panes vitae pastos, Facias nos faece Carnis dempta castos.

2. Sumens sacrum fermentum Ad salutem omen
Nostrum delens fletum, Mutans Evae nomen.

4. Monstra, quod sis mater Matris, per quam sumens
Fili us et pater Tulis esse tutus.

6. Vitam nostram munda, Ut sic glorie e mur
Et luce jucunda Semper col laetemur.

7. Sit laus et honoris Soli Deo munus, Nunc et cunctis horis Tribus honor unus.

49
A- - - - - -
A- - - - - - men, a- - - -
A- - -
A- - - - men, a- - - -
58
- - men, a- - - - men.
- - men, a- - - - - men.
- - men, a- - - men, a- men.
-men, a- - - men, a- men.

43. Christe redemptor omnium, Conserva

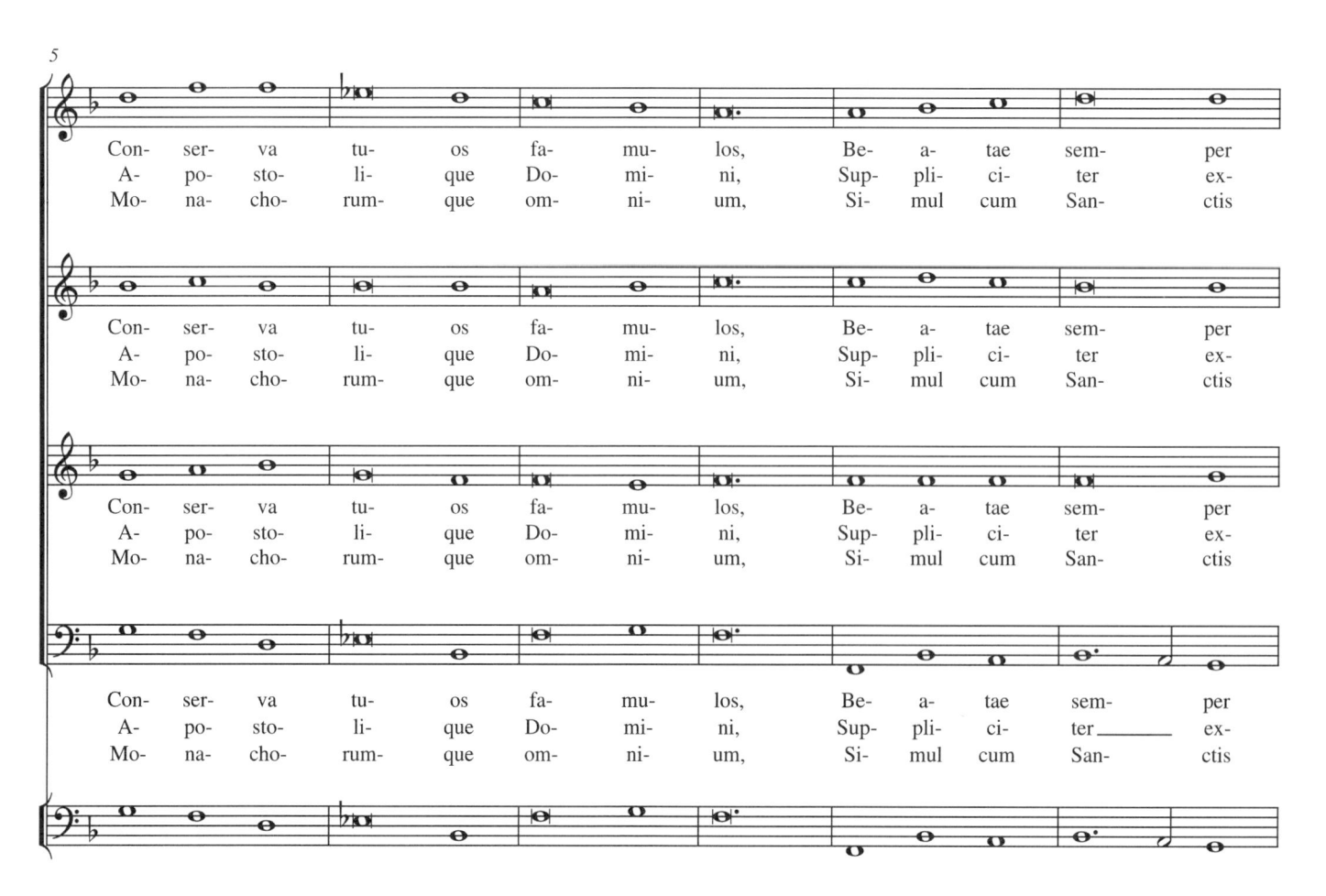

[Dessus 1]
[Dessus 2]
[Haute-contre]
[Basse]
[Orgue]

1. Chri- ste re- dem- ptor om- ni- um,
3. Va- tes ae- ter- ni Ju- di- cis,
5. Cho- ri san- cta- rum Vir- gi- num,

Con- ser- va tu- os fa- mu- los, Be- a- tae sem- per
A- po- sto- li- que Do- mi- ni, Sup- pli- ci- ter ex-
Mo- na- cho- rum- que om- ni- um, Si- mul cum San- ctis

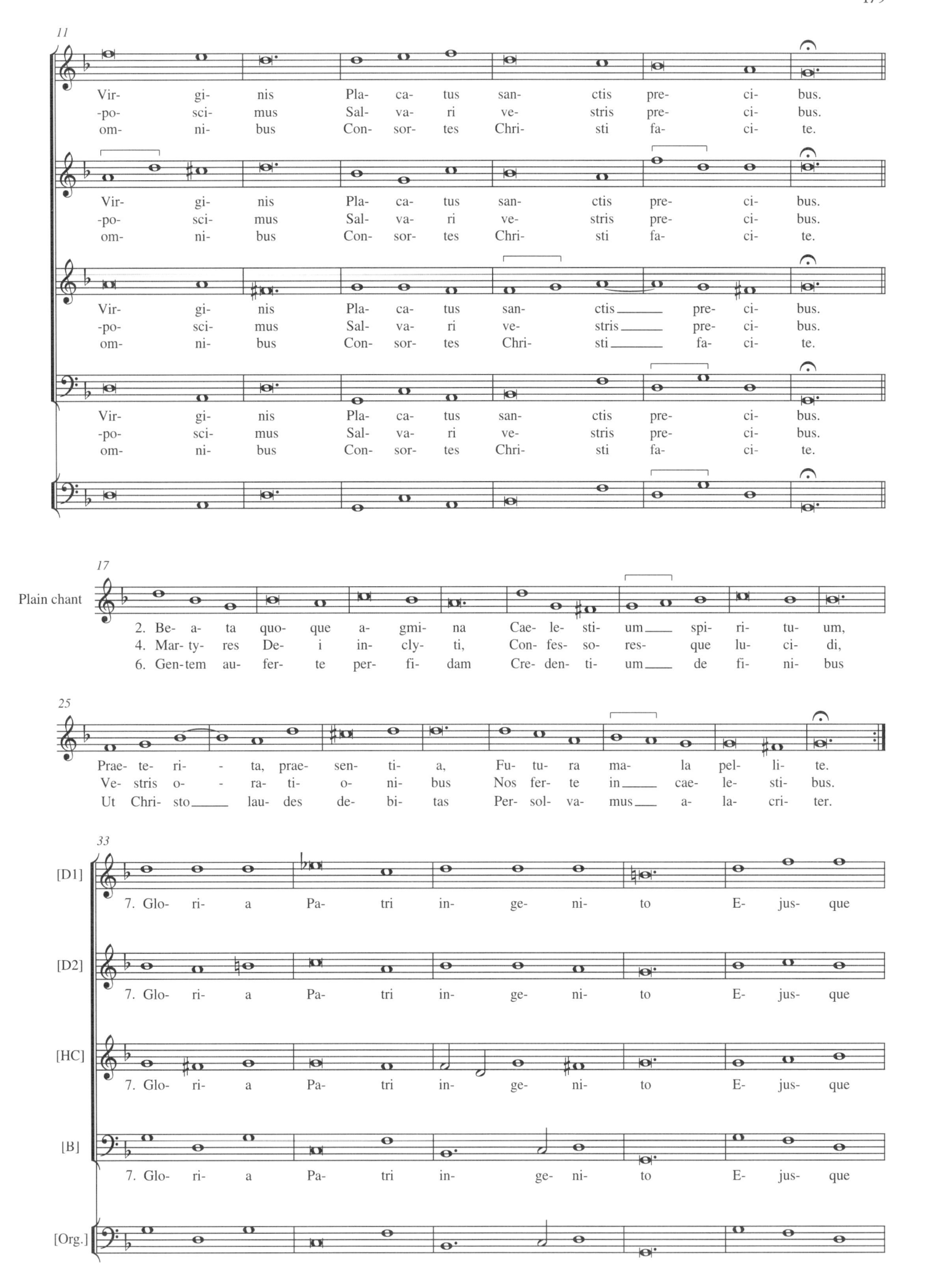

Vir- gi- nis Pla- ca- tus san- ctis pre- ci- bus.
-po- sci- mus Sal- va- ri ve- stris pre- ci- bus.
om- ni- bus Con- sor- tes Chri- sti fa- ci- te.

Plain chant:

2. Be- a- ta quo- que a- gmi- na Cae- le- sti- um spi- ri- tu- um,
4. Mar- ty- res De- i in- cly- ti, Con- fes- so- res- que lu- ci- di,
6. Gen- tem au- fer- te per- fi- dam Cre- den- ti- um de fi- nibus

Prae- te- ri- ta, prae- sen- ti- a, Fu- tu- ra ma- la pel- li- te.
Ve- stris o- ra- ti- o- ni- bus Nos fer- te in cae- le- sti- bus.
Ut Chri- sto lau- des de- bi- tas Per- sol- va- mus a- la- cri- ter.

7. Glo- ri- a Pa- tri in- ge- ni- to E- jus- que

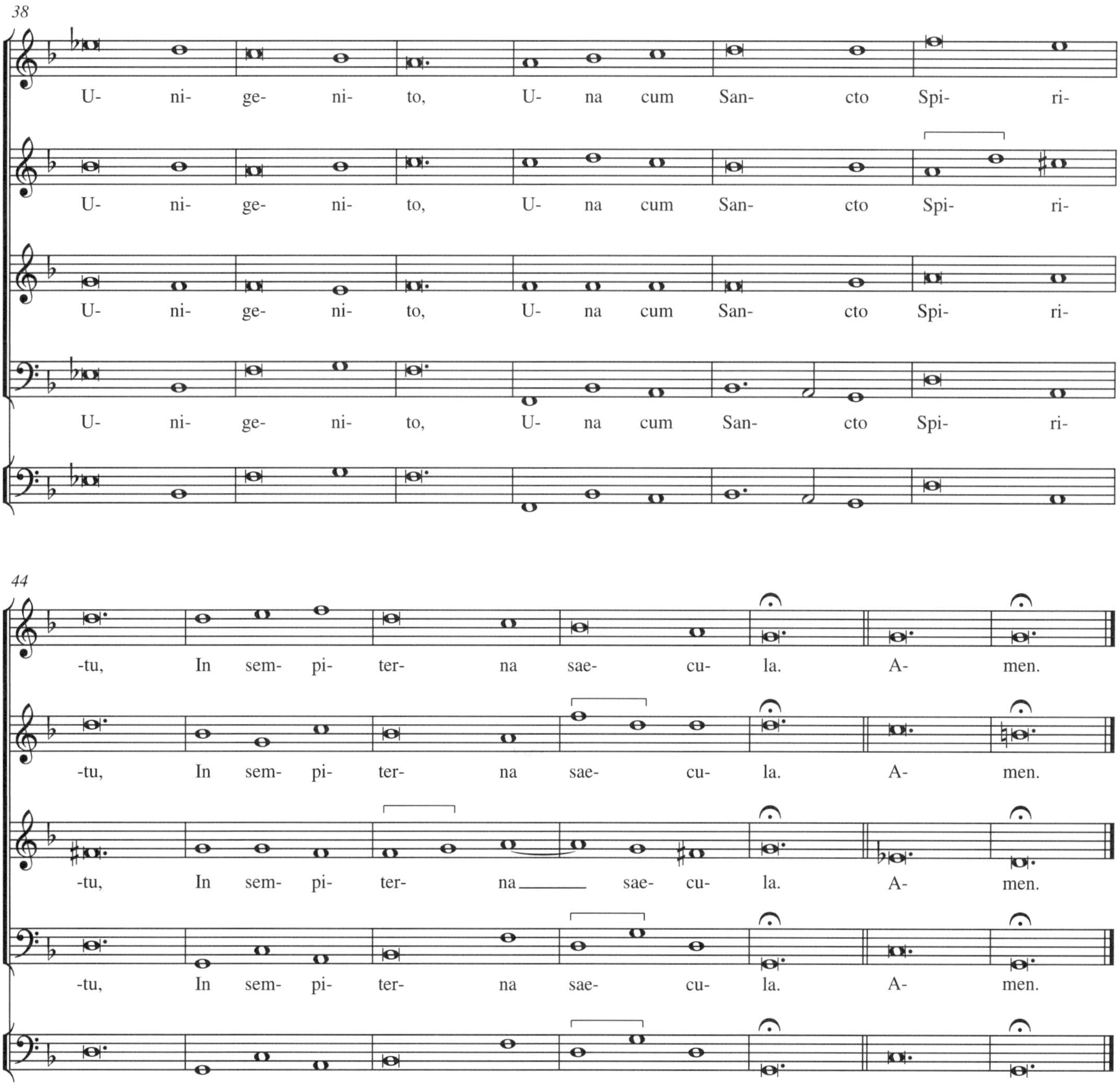
38
U- ni- ge- ni- to, U- na cum San- cto Spi- ri-
U- ni- ge- ni- to, U- na cum San- cto Spi- ri-
U- ni- ge- ni- to, U- na cum San- cto Spi- ri-
U- ni- ge- ni- to, U- na cum San- cto Spi- ri-
44
-tu, In sem- pi- ter- na sae- cu- la. A- men.
-tu, In sem- pi- ter- na sae- cu- la. A- men.
-tu, In sem- pi- ter- na sae- cu- la. A- men.
-tu, In sem- pi- ter- na sae- cu- la. A- men.

44. Christe redemptor omnium, Ex Patre

1. Chri- ste re- demp- tor om- ni- um, Ex Pa- tre, Pa- tris u- ni- ce, So- lus an- te prin- ci- pi- um Na- tus in- ef- fa- bi- li- ter.

2. Tu lumen, tu splendor Patris,
   Tu spes perennis omnium:
   Intende quos fundunt preces
   Tui per orbem famuli.

3. Memento salutis Auctor,
   Quod nostri quondam corporis,
   Ex illibata Virgine
   Nascendo, formam sumpseris.

4. Hic praesens testatur dies,
   Currens per anni circulum,
   Quod solus a sede Patris
   Mundi salus adveneris.

5. Hunc caelum, terra, hunc mare,
   Hunc omne quod in eis est,
   Auctorem adventus tui
   Laudans exsultat cantico.

6. Nos quoque, qui sancto tuo
   Redempti sanguine sumus,
   Ob diem natalis tui
   Hymnum novum concinimus.

7. Gloria tibi Domine,
   Qui natus est de Virgine,
   Cum Patre et Sancto Spiritu,
   In sempiterna saecula.

45. Claris conjubila

1. Claris conjubila Gallia laudibus, Laeteris Benedicti Patris ossibus, Felixque gremio condita patria, Servas membra celebria.

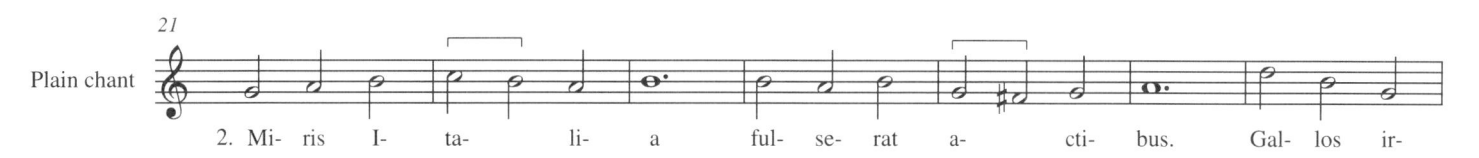

Plain chant: 2. Mi- ris I- ta- li- a ful- se- rat a- cti- bus. Gal- los ir- -ra- di- at cor- po- re mor- tu- us; Si- gnis ad tu- mu- -lum cre- bri- us e- mi- cat, Il- lu- strans pa- tri- am no- vam.

[D1] 3. Hic va- tum ve- te- rum fa- cta re- su- sci- tat, Mor- ti, quod li- bu-
[D2] 3. Hic va- tum ve- te- rum fa- cta re- su- sci- tat, Mor- ti, quod li- bu-
[HC] 3. Hic va- tum ve- te- rum fa- cta re- su- sci- tat, Mor- ti, quod li- bu-
[B] 3. Hic va- tum ve- te- rum fa- cta re- su- sci- tat, Mor- ti, quod li- bu-
Org.

-it,_____ mor- tu- us im- pe- rat; Ex- tin- ctum pro- pri-
-it,_____ mor- tu- us im- pe- rat; Ex- tin- ctum pro- pri-
-it,_____ mor- tu- us im- pe- rat; Ex- tin- ctum pro- pri-
-it,_____ mor- tu- us im- pe- rat; Ex- tin- ctum pro- pri-

-us os- si- bus ex- ci- tat: O quam mi- ra po- ten- ti- a.

-us os- si- bus ex- ci- tat: O quam mi- ra po- ten- ti- a.

-us os- si- bus ex- ci- tat: O quam mi- ra po- ten- ti- a.

-us os- si- bus ex- ci- tat: O quam mi- ra po- ten- ti- a.

Plain chant

4. Jam cae- lo re- si- dens, o Pa- ter o- pti- me, Di- vi- nis fa- mu- los im- bu- e re- gu- lis, An- gu- stum per i- -ter scan- de- re lar- gi- us Do- na re- gna pe- ren- ni- a.

[D1] 5. Cun- cto- rum do- mi- nans om- ni- po- ten- ti- a, Quae de

[D2] 5. Cun- cto- rum do- mi- nans om- ni- po- ten- ti- a, Quae de

[HC] 5. Cun- cto- rum do- mi- nans om- ni- po- ten- ti- a, Quae de

[B] 5. Cun- cto- rum do- mi- nans om- ni- po- ten- ti- a, Quae de

Org.

96
se- de po- li con- spi-cis om- ni- a: Psal- len- tum pla- ci- de
se- de po- li con- spi-cis om- ni- a: Psal- len- tum pla- ci- de
se- de po- li con- spi-cis om- ni- a: Psal- len- tum pla- ci- de
se- de po- li con- spi-cis om- ni- a: Psal- len- tum pla- ci- de
103
su- sci- pe can- ti- ca, Vo- tis, vo- ce pre- can- ti- a.
su- sci- pe can- ti- ca, Vo- tis, vo- ce pre- can- ti- a.
su- sci- pe can- ti- ca, Vo- tis, vo- ce pre- can- ti- a.
su- sci- pe can- ti- ca, Vo- tis, vo- ce pre- can- ti- a.
110
A- - - - - - - - - - - men.
A- - - - - - - - men.
A- - - - men.
A- - - - - men.

46. Dionysii martyris

1. Di- o- ny- si- i mar- ty- ris Et so- ci- o- rum me- ri- ta,
Cum cle- ro can- tat ce- le- bris Con- ven- tus in Ec- cle- si- a.

2. Ad Gal- los mis- si prin- ci- pes, Cae- le- stis lu- men glo- ri- ae
Per gra- dus Ar- chi- prae- si- des Spar- ge- bant tres Lu- te- ti- ae.

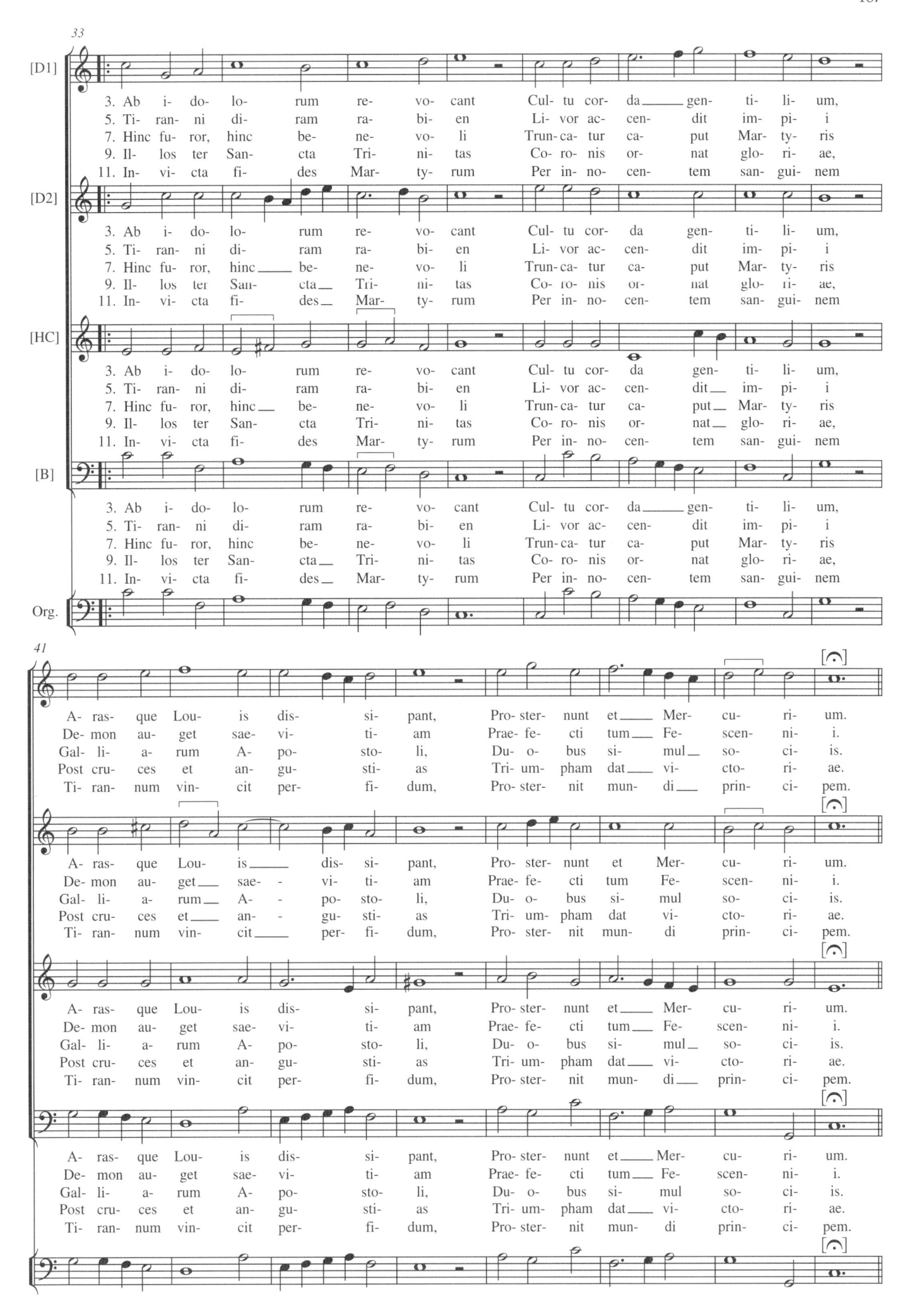

3. Ab idolorum revocant Cultu corda gentilium,
5. Tiranni diram rabien Livor accendit impii
7. Hinc furor, hinc benevoli Truncatur caput Martyris
9. Illos ter Sancta Trinitas Coronis ornat gloriae,
11. Invicta fides Martyrum Per innocentem sanguinem

Arasque Lou is dissipant, Prosternunt et Mercurium.
Demon auget saevitiam Praefecti tum Fescennii.
Galliarum Apostoli, Duobus simul sociis.
Post cruces et angustias Triumpham dat victoriae.
Tirannum vincit perfidum, Prosternit mundi principem.

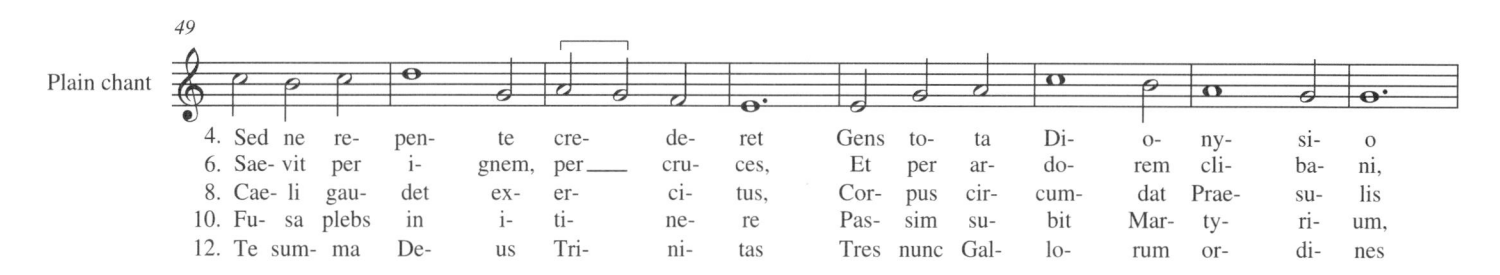

Plain chant

4. Sed ne re- pen- te cre- de- ret Gens to- ta Di- o- ny- si- o
6. Sae- vit per i- gnem, per cru- ces, Et per ar- do- rem cli- ba- ni,
8. Cae- li gau- det ex- er- ci- tus, Cor- pus cir- cum- dat Prae- su- lis
10. Fu- sa plebs in i- ti- ne- re Pas- sim su- bit Mar- ty- ri- um,
12. Te sum- ma De- us Tri- ni- tas Tres nunc Gal- lo- rum or- di- nes

Et Cle- men- tis se sub- de- ret Ro- ma- ni Pon- ti- fi- ci- o,
Per ro- tas, et fe- ras tru- ces; San- ctis sed cre- scunt a- ni- mi.
Dum ca- put ge- stat ma- ni- bus Sa- cris et lu- dit can- ti- cis.
Per vi- cos cae- pit flu- e- re San- guis cae- so- rum cor- po- rum.
Pre- ca- mur sem- per fo- ve- as Hos per tres Ar- chi- Mar- ti- res.

[D1] 13. Fi- dem pro- fes- sos a- spi- ce For- ti re-

[D2] 13. Fi- dem pro- fes- sos a- spi- ce For- ti re-

[HC]

[B]

Org.

-dem- ptos bra- chi- o Di- o- ny- si- o au- spi- ce

-dem- ptos bra- chi- o Di- o- ny- si- o au- spi- ce

Di- o- ny- si- o au- spi- ce

Di- o- ny- si- o au- spi- ce

76
Da fru- i cae- li gau- di- a. A-
Da fru- i cae- li gau- di- a.
Da fru- i cae- li gau- di- a.
Da fru- i cae- li gau- di- a.
82
- men, a- men, a- men.
A- - men, a- men.
A- - men, a- men.
A- - men.

47. Iste Confessor

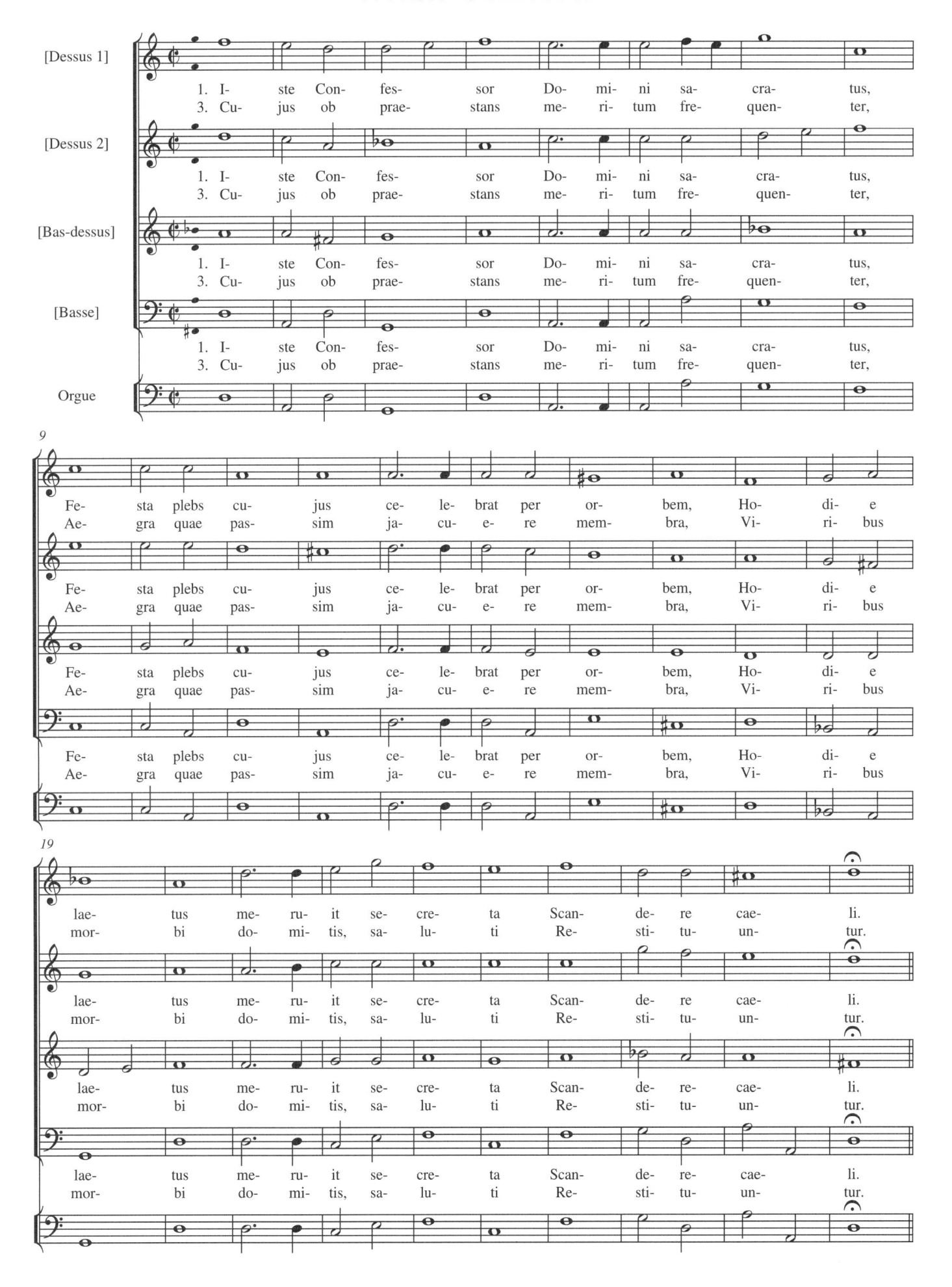

1. I- ste Confessor Domini sacratus,
Festa plebs cujus celebrat per orbem,
Hodie laetus meruit secreta
Scandere caeli.

3. Cujus ob praestans meritum frequenter,
Aegra quae passim jacuere membra,
Viribus morbi domitis, saluti
Restituuntur.

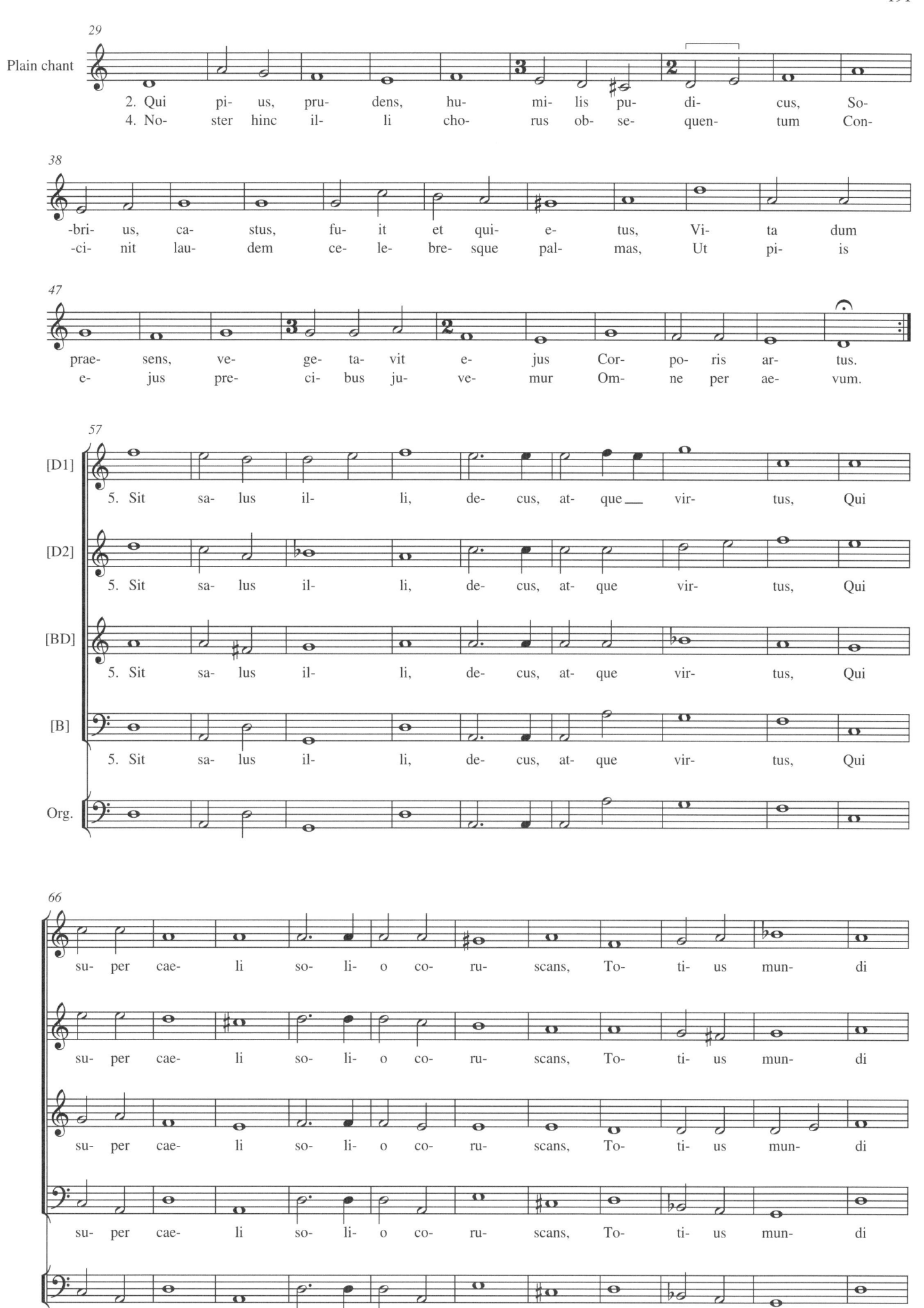

2. Qui pius, prudens, humilis pudicus, Sobrius, castus, fuit et quietus, Vita dum praesens, vegetavit ejus Corporis artus.

4. Noster hinc illi chorus obsequentum Concinit laudem celebresque palmas, Ut piis ejus precibus juvemur Omne per aevum.

5. Sit salus illi, decus, atque virtus, Qui super caeli solio coruscans, Totius mundi

77
se- ri- em gu- ber- nat, Tri- nus et u- nus.
se- ri- em gu- ber- nat, Tri- nus et u- nus.
se- ri- em gu- ber- nat, Tri- nus et u- nus.
se- ri- em gu- ber- nat, Tri- nus et u- nus.
86
A- - - men, a-
A- - men, a- -
A- - men, a- men, a- men,
A- - - men, a- - men, a-
91
- men, a- - - men.
- - men, a- - men.
a- - - men, a- men.
- men, a- - men, a- - men.

48. Jesu, nostra redemptio

1. Jesu, nostra redemptio, Amor et desiderium, Deus Creator omnium, Homo in fine temporum.

3. Inferni claustra penetrans, Tuos captivos redimens, Victor triumpho nobili Ad dextram Patris residens:

2. Quae te vicit clementia, Ut ferres nostra crimina, Crudelem mortem patiens, Ut nos a morte tolleres!

4. Ipsa te cogat pietas, Ut mala nostra superes Parcendo, et voti compotes Nos tuo vultu saties.

5. Tu esto nostrum gaudium, Qui es futurus praemium: Sit nostra in te Glori-

-a Per cuncta semper saecula.

-a Per cuncta semper saecula.

-a Per cuncta semper saecula.

-a Per cuncta semper saecula.

A- - - - men, a-

A-

A- - - men,

A-

54
- - - men,
- men, a- -
a- - - -
a- - men, a-
- men, a- - - men,
58
a- - men, a- men, a- men.
- - men, a- - men, a- men.
- men, a- men, a- men.
- men, a- - men.
a- - - - men.

49. O gloriosae virgines

1. O gloriosae virgines, Cum angelis jam divites, Sponsa tenetis Dominum, Caelum cubile sanctum.

2. Quod gessistis jam habetis,

Nobis adeste miseris, Ut nos absolvat Dominus, absolvat Dominus, Per vos cunctis criminibus, cunctis criminibus. Alleluja.

50. O salutaris hostia

21
-munt ho- sti- li- a,
Da ro- - bur, fer au- - xi-
-munt ho- sti- li- a,
Da ro- bur, fer au- xi-
pre- munt ho- sti- - li- a,
-munt ho- sti- li- a,
29
- li- um,
Da ro- bur, fer au- xi- - li- um.
- li- um,
Da ro- bur, fer au- xi- - li- um.
Da ro- - bur, fer au- xi- - li- um.
Da ro- - bur, fer au- xi- - li- um.

51. Pange lingua … Corporis

21
- sque pre- ti- o- si, Quem in mun- - di
pre- ti- o- - si, Quem in mun- di pre-
-sque pre- ti- o- si, Quem in mun- di pre-
-sque pre- ti- o- si, Quem in mun- - di
28
pre- - ti- um Fru- - ctus ven-
- - ti- um Fru- - ctus ven-
- - ti- um Fru- - ctus ven- -
pre- - ti- um Fru- ctus ven- -
35
-tris ge- ne- ro- si Rex ef- fu- dit gen- ti- um.
-tris ge- ne- ro- si Rex ef- fu- dit gen- ti- um.
-tris ge- ne- ro- si Rex ef- fu- dit gen- ti- um.
-tris ge- ne- ro- si Rex ef- fu- dit gen- ti- um.

43
[D1]
2. No- - bis da- - tus, no- - bis
[D2]
2. No- bis da- tus, no- - bis
Org.
50
na- tus, Ex in- ta- cta Vir- gi- ne,
na- tus, Ex in- ta- cta Vir- -
57
Et in mun- do con- ver- sa- tus,
- gi- ne,
65
Spar- so ver- bi se- mi- ne, Su- i mo-
Spar- so ver- bi se- mi- ne,

-ras ____ in- co- la- tus Mi- ro clau- sit or- di- ne.

Mi- ro clau- sit or- di- ne.

[D1] A- - - - men.

[D2] A- - men.

[HC] A- - - men, a- - men. ____

[B] A- men. ____

Org.

52. Pange lingua ... Certaminis

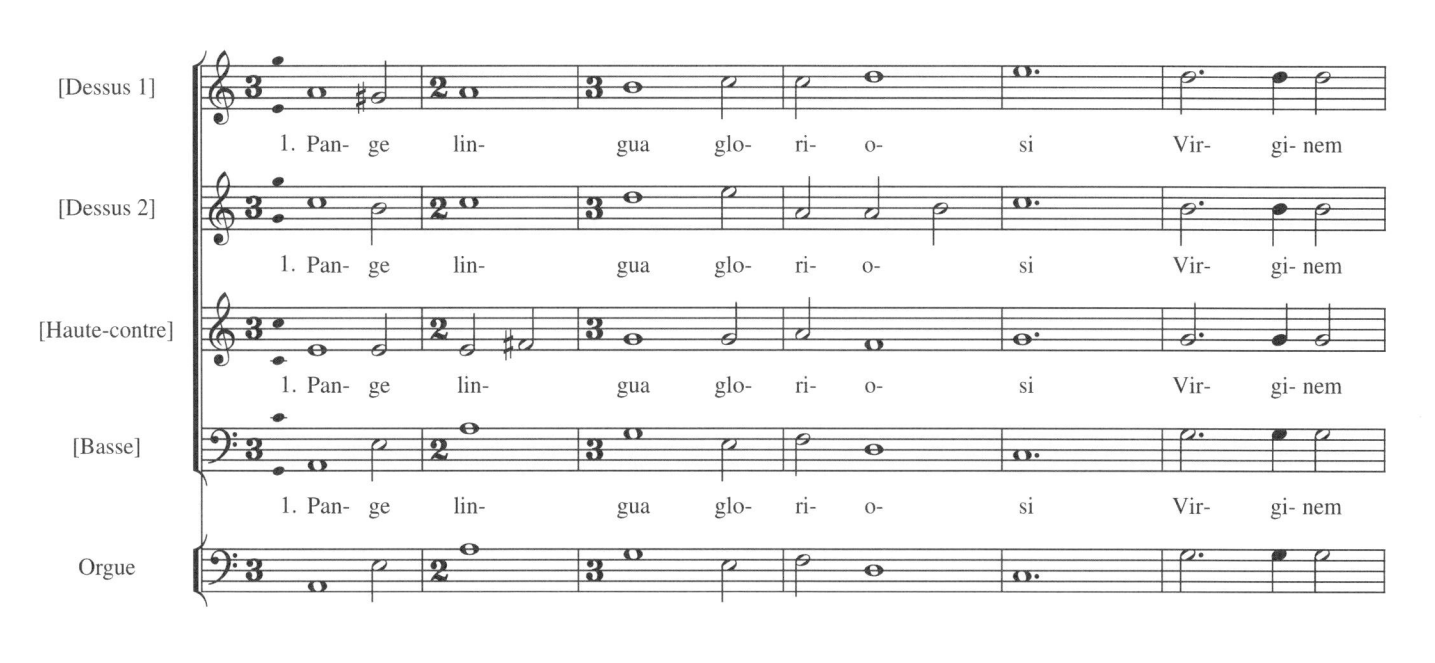

*For a plainchant setting of verse 2, see the appendix.

Nuptiis dignata sponsi Se sacris miscet choris.

Amen, amen, amen, amen.

53. Quam pulchra es

*For an alternative refrain for four voices, see no. 53a.

Fine

1. O gloriosa domina, Excelsa super sidera:
Qui te creavit, provide, Lactasti sacro ubere.

D.C. "Quam pulchra es," etc.

2. Quod Eva tristis abstulit, Tu reddis almo germine:
Intrent ut astra flebiles, Caeli fenestra facta es.

D.C. "Quam pulchra es," etc.

53a. Quam pulchra es (alternative refrain)

54. Veni Creator Spiritus

2. Qui di- ce- ris Pa- ra- cli- tus, Al- tis- si- mi do- num De- i, Fons vi- vus, i- gnis, ca- ri- tas, Et spi- ri- ta- lis un- cti- o.

3. Tu se- pti- for- mis mu- ne- re, De- xtrae De- -i tu di- gi- tus, Tu ri- te pro- mis- sum Pa- tris, Ser- mo- ne di- tans gut- tu- ra.

4. Ac- cen- de lu- men sen-si-bus, In-fun-de a-mo-rem cor-di-bus, In- fir- ma no- stri cor-po- ris, Vir- tu- te fir-mas per- pe- ti.

5. Ho- stem re- pel- las lon- gi- us, Pa- cem- que do- nes pro- ti- nus: Du- cto- re sic te prae- vi- o, Vi- te- mus om- ne no- xi- um.

6. Per te sciamus da Patrem, Noscamus atque Filium, Teque utrisque Spiritum Credamus omni tempore.

7. Gloria Patri Domino, Natoque qui a mortuis, Surrexit, ac Paraclito, In saeculorum saecula.

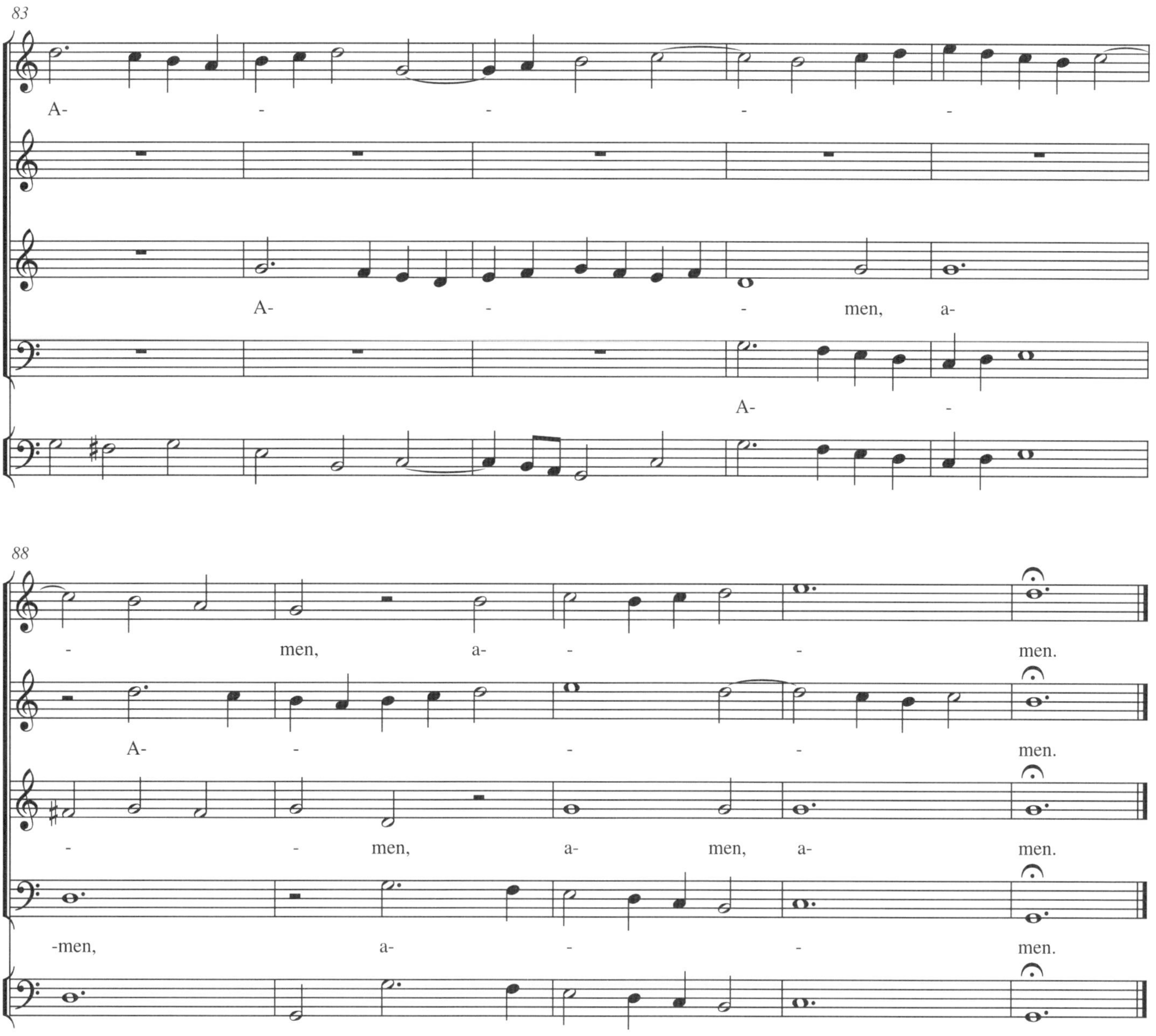
83
A- - - - -
A- - - men, a-
A- -
88
- men, a- - - men.
A- - - men.
- - men, a- men, a- men.
-men, a- - - men.

Critical Report

Sources

The music of this edition has been taken from the manuscript Paris, Bibliothèque nationale de France, Département de la Musique, Rés. V^{ma} ms. 571, a bound volume of 239 folios containing some three hundred sacred Latin works in score. The manuscript was copied and assembled by organist and composer André Pechon from the 1630s through the 1680s, and while most of the works in the collection are preserved anonymously, over seventy can be attributed to Antoine Boesset. (Other composers attributed in the source include Carissimi, Bouzignac, Dumont, and Moulinié.) For more information about the precise dating of the manuscript contents and the attribution to Antoine Boesset, see " 'Boesset' Attributions in Rés. 571" and table 2 in the introduction.

Editorial Methods

This edition includes all works in Rés. 571 that can be attributed to Boesset, with the exception of those made up primarily of fauxbourdon and those that are small parts of lengthy chant works: "De profundis" (fol. 56v), "Lauda Jerusalem" (fols. 146v–147r), polyphonic settings of Hebrew letters for Tenebrae (fols. 183v–186v), Nunc dimittis (fols. 215r–v), and "Stabat mater" (fols. 215v–216r). As there is little systematic organization of Boesset's music within the source, this edition has reordered works so that they are organized first by genre, then in alphabetical order within genre, and finally in chronological order of copying. This system has been modified for parallel settings (i.e., mixed-voice and high-voice versions of the same piece), which appear in sequence. Folio numbers of the source are in the critical commentary. With the exception of the three masses, titles are editorial and are based on the textual incipit. The source includes the indications "à 4" and "à 5" for many of the works; these have been removed without comment.

Spelling, punctuation, and capitalization have been standardized and modernized in accordance with the *Liber Usualis* and the *Antiphonale Monasticum*. Source abbreviations and repetitions of text indicated only by an idem sign (*ij.*) or the first syllable or word of a phrase (e.g., "Al." = Alleluja) have been realized tacitly unless they are in some way questionable or ambiguous. Where voices are untexted, the underlay is usually so clear that text has been inserted tacitly; when the underlay is ambiguous, a note has been made in the critical commentary. Source slurs used to indicate text underlay in untexted voices have been removed without comment. Ligatures in the source also indicate text underlay and are shown by full horizontal brackets. Word division follows modern rules for singing in Latin.

All voice names are editorial and appear in brackets, with two exceptions: the "Org." indications that appear in the late-copied section of the manuscript (expanded to "Orgue" without comment in the edition), and the designation "Plain chant," which appears in some chant sections of Rés. 571 and has been tacitly added to all chant versets for the alternatim hymns. Voice names have been suggested in accordance with the clef of each part as follows:

    Dessus = G2
    Bas-dessus = C1
    Haute-contre = C2
    Haute-taille = C3
    Taille = C4
    Basse = F3 or F4
    Basse continue and Orgue = F3 or F4

Treble clef has been substituted for C1 and C2 clefs; transposing treble clef for C3 and C4 clefs; and bass clef for F3 and F4 clefs. The range of each voice appears after the modern clef, key signature, and time signature. The bass voice and basse continue part share a staff in the source. The edition has separated these onto two staves and has tacitly altered the duration of notes in the bass voice at the ends of phrases to align with the upper parts. In some cases, the duration of notes at the ends of phrases in other voices has been altered to be consistent with the surrounding parts and has been reported in the critical commentary.

Repetition schemes in the source have been tacitly modernized and clarified. The source typically indicates first and second endings by showing the first few notes and/or text of the repeated passage following the end of the piece; in many cases, either the term "segno" or a 𝄋 also serve to guide the performer. These indications have been converted to modern first and second endings without comment. Source directives such as "Sanctus ut supra" have been replaced with modern da capo or dal segno indications without brackets. When necessary, repeated sections have been written out and reported in the critical commentary. If the repetition scheme in the source is ambiguous, editorial suggestions have been provided in brackets.

This edition includes both through-composed and strophic hymns. Hymn verses are numbered in the edition to clarify the structure of each work, and double barlines have been added at the end of each strophe. While through-composed hymns in the source include text underlay for all verses intended for performance, most strophic hymns contain text underlay for only one or (in the case of alternatim hymns) two verses. As it should be presumed that all hymn verses were meant to be sung, the remaining verses have been included in the edition either as additional lines of text underlay or as residual texts at the end of each hymn. For alternatim hymn settings, even-numbered verses should be sung as chant; odd-numbered verses in polyphony. For alternatim hymns with an odd number of verses, the remaining verses appear as additional lines of text underlay, and the final polyphonic verse has been written out to clarify the repetition scheme; these instances are reported in the critical commentary.

Chant versets for the alternatim hymns have been taken from the source, which provides rhythmicized hymn melodies grouped together at fols. 218v–219r (see plate 4). Most of these hymn melodies are melodically concordant with those found in the *Antiphonier . . . de Montmartre*, but the printed source lacks barlines and time signatures. The source does not provide a chant verset for a single alternatim hymn, "Veni Creator Spiritus." In this case, the chant melody has been taken from the *Antiphonier . . . de Montmartre* and converted to white notation. While the edition replicates the breves and semibreves of the *Antiphonier . . . de Montmartre,* no attempt has been made to impose a regular meter upon these versets. For more information about the appropriate performance of chant rhythms, see "Notes on Performance" in the introduction.

The edition reflects the original barring of the source for all the polyphonic works, but barlines have been added tacitly to the rhythmicized hymn versets if they were missing from Rés. 571. The appearance of barlines in the source differs according to copying period, and the method of transcribing double barlines varies throughout the edition. In works copied during the early and middle periods of the manuscript (fols. 1v–177v; see table 2 in the introduction), the paper is pre-ruled from top to bottom with barlines (see plates 1 and 2); in some places, Pechon drew an additional barline by hand to indicate the end of a section—though the additional barline did not always appear in all parts. Regardless of whether this hand-drawn barline appeared in all or in only some voices, these barlines have been transcribed as double barlines in the edition. For the late-copied group of works, the paper was ruled as the copying proceeded, but, again, Pechon drew an additional barline by hand at major structural divisions. These places have also been rendered as double barlines in the edition. Exceptions to this policy are reported in the critical commentary. Occasionally Pechon placed the equivalent of two measures between pre-ruled barlines, especially when approaching the end of a line. In these cases, missing barlines have been tacitly added.

The time signatures of the source—**C**, ¢, **2**, and **3**—have been retained wherever possible; ¢ therefore appears with both two half notes and four half notes per measure. Proportional time signatures, such as ¢**3**, have been converted to their modern equivalent, and the original time signature appears above the staff. For shifts between duple and triple meter in which the tactus (rather than the beat) remains constant, an equivalency has been provided above the staff.

The original note values are used, that is, transcription is at the ratio 1:1, with two exceptions: first, passages with coloration have been reduced at a ratio of either 4:1 or 2:1; second, some alternatim hymn verses have been reduced at a ratio of 2:1. In both cases, these reductions aim to improve readability and ease transitions between sections; all reductions and (when applicable) the original meters in the affected passages are reported in the critical commentary. Notes that continue past a barline in the source have been divided into appropriate values and connected with a tie. Final notes of sections or whole works have been regularized to a whole note with a fermata, unless a moving voice requires the note to be longer than notated in the source. Fermatas do not always appear consistently in all parts; when they appear in only one part, they have been tacitly realized in the remaining parts. Editorial fermatas appear in brackets. Source beaming, which often indicates text underlay, has been changed to conform to modern beaming practices.

Source accidentals are typically valid only for the note itself and any immediate or very close repetition; in the edition, accidentals follow the modern practice by which they are valid for the entire measure in which they occur. Editorial accidentals are enclosed in square brackets; added cautionary accidentals appear in parentheses. Accidentals made superfluous by modern barring and convention have been eliminated without comment.

Critical Commentary

Critical notes list rejected or ambiguous readings from the source and alternative readings taken from the *Antiphonier . . . de Montmartre*. Notes are located in the score by measure number and part name. When specific notes and rests in a measure are cited, tied noteheads are numbered individually, and rests are counted separately from notes. The following abbreviations are used in the paragraphs below: M(m). = measure(s), D1–3 = Dessus 1–3, BD = Bas-dessus, HC = Haute-contre, HT = Haute-taille, T = Taille, B = Basse, B.c. = Basse continue, Org. = Orgue. The pitch system used throughout is that in which c' represents middle C.

1. Alma Redemptoris Mater

Source. Fols. 199v–200r.

Notes. M. 12, D1, note 4 is d". M. 25, D1, note 1 is half note followed by quarter rest. M. 30, D2, note 4 to m. 31, note 1, slur.

2. Anna mater Matris

Source. Fols. 55v–56r.

Comment. Marked "Boesset" in Pechon's hand.

Notes. M. 28, B.c., rhythm unclear. Mm. 54–56, D2, "tuo" missing; source underlay as follows: m. 54, note 3 through m. 55, note 1, "so-"; m. 55, note 2, "-ci-"; m. 55, note 3 through m. 56, note 1, "-a-"; m. 56, note 2, "-ri."

3. Ave Maria (1)

Source. Fols. 152r–v.

Comment. Mixed-voice paraphrase of "Ave Maria (2)."

Notes. M. 9, D1, whole note. M. 12, HC, note 1 is f♯'. M. 15, HT, note 3 is half note. M. 27, meter is **3**. M. 29, B and B.c., source provides music for each part. M. 66, breve in all parts.

4. Ave Maria (2)

Source. Fols. 153v–154r.

Comment. High-voice paraphrase of "Ave Maria (1)."

Note. M. 11, D2 and HC, whole note.

5. Ave per cor suavissimum Jesu

Source. Fols. 187v–188r.

6. Ave Regina caelorum

Source. Fols. 200r–v.

Note. M. 51, D2, whole note.

7. Ave salus mundi

Source. Fols. 194v–195r.

Comment. The presence of superfluous flats and necessary addition of editorial naturals suggests that this piece may have been intended to be written without a key signature.

8. Ave virginum gemma Catharina

Source. Fols. 207r–v.

9. Benedicimus te

Source. Fols. 208r–v.

Notes. M. 14, HC, notes 1–3 are e'–d'–d'. Mm. 35–39, source has "exibemus" instead of "exhibemus."

10. Domine salvum fac regem (1)

Source. Fols. 175r–v.

Comment. Mixed-voice version of "Domine salvum fac regem (2)."

Notes. Mm. 16–17, HT, "et" missing from underlay; text is "die exaudi"; note 1 is dotted half note; rhythm changed to correct underlay. M. 29, B.c., note 2 is editorial.

11. Domine salvum fac regem (2)

Source. Fol. 1v.

Comments. Marked "Boesset" in Pechon's hand. High-voice version of "Domine salvum fac regem (1)."

Notes. M. 11, D1, half note followed by half rest. Mm. 13–14, D1, underlay as follows: m. 13, notes 3–4, "au-"; m. 13, note 5 through m. 14, note 1, "-di"; m. 14, note 2, "nos"; m. 14, note 3, "in"; m. 14, note 4, "di-". M. 18, D2, whole note. M. 21, D2, notes 1–2, rhythm is quarter note, 8th rest, 8th note. M. 28, B and B.c., notes missing.

12. Domine salvum fac regem (3)

Source. Fols. 196v–197r.

Notes. M. 36, "Et exaudi nos ut supra" and "Et ex. cy dessus," 𝄋, and first few notes of m. 11 appear at end of measure; repetition of mm. 11–27 written out in edition as mm. 37–53.

13. Domine salvum fac regem (4)

Source. Fol. 197r.

Notes. Mm. 17–23, B, underlay cut off. M. 22, D2, slur across entire measure.

14. Duo seraphim

Source. Fols. 203r–v.

Note. M. 72, D1, half note followed by half rest.

14a. Duo seraphim (alternative opening)

Source. Fol. 203v.

Notes. Mm. 4–5, D1, rhythmic errors resulting in displaced barlines; source rhythm as follows: m. 4, half note and four 8th notes; m. 5 (incomplete), half note followed by quarter note. M. 14, all parts, fermata.

15. Ecce panis Angelorum

Source. Fol. 165v.

16. Fons aquae vivae

Source. Fols. 165v–167r.

Notes. Mm. 5–7, B, source suggests text underlay, but impossible to align text with notes. Mm. 12–16, coloration in source; reduced 4:1 in edition. M. 21, BD, note 1 is quarter note; divided into two 8th notes to fit text underlay. Mm. 23–27, coloration in source; reduced 4:1 in edition. M. 35, D2, notes 1–2 are g♯'. M. 50, D2, half note followed by half rest. M. 84, double barline. Mm. 87–88, D2, notes are tied.

17. Hic est beatissimus

Source. Fols. 204r–v.

Notes. M. 12, D2, whole note. M. 31, D1, note 3 is d♯". M. 42, "Caeteris &c ut supra" in source; repetition of mm. 18–26 written out in edition.

18. *O athletum invictissimum*

Source. Fols. 204v–205v.

Notes. M. 19, B and B.c., notes are editorial; source has only underlay. Mm. 24–28, coloration in source; reduced 4:1 in edition. M. 48, D3, notes 3–4 are 8th notes. M. 49, D3, whole note.

19. *O crux ave*

Source. Fols. 195v–196r.

Notes. M. 7, B, note 1, underlay continues "spes" from m. 6. M. 7, B, note 2 through m. 8, note 1, underlay is "ave."

20. *O Doctor optime*

Source. Fols. 205v–206v.

Notes. M. 6, D1, half note followed by half rest. M. 7, Org., note 1 is e. M. 41, single barline.

21. *O Pastor aeterne*

Source. Fols. 206v–207r.

Note. M. 4, D2, note 5 is a′.

22. *O quam suavis*

Source. Fols. 193v–194r.

23. *O sacrum convivium*

Source. Fols. 195r–v.

Note. Mm. 26–34, coloration in source; reduced 4:1 in edition.

24. *Popule meus*

Source. Fols. 181v–182r.

25. *Pretiosus Domini Dionysius*

Source. Fols. 198r–v.

Notes. M. 36, B.c., note 3 is e. Mm. 53–54, B.c., notes are d–c–d–c–B–e.

26. *Regina caeli (1)*

Source. Fols. 149v–150v.

Comment. Mixed-voice version of "Regina caeli (2)."

Notes. M. 32, double barline. M. 36, B.c., note 1 is f. M. 41, double barline.

27. *Regina caeli (2)*

Source. Fols. 202v–203r.

Comment. High-voice version of "Regina caeli (1)."

Notes. M. 20, D2, note 2 is d′. M. 37, fermata and double barline.

28. *Regina caeli (3)*

Source. Fols. 221r–v.

Comments. HC appears below HT in the source. The scoring is G2, C2, C3, F3; as such it would have been performable by both the Montmartre and *musique de la chambre* ensembles.

29. *Regnum mundi*

Source. Fols. 208v–209r.

Notes. M. 33, "In quem" text only in source; repetition of mm. 15–19 written out in edition as mm. 33–37. M. 43, "Regnum mundi ut supra" and "Regnum mundi da capo" in source; repetition of mm. 1–19 written out in edition as mm. 44–62.

30. *Salve Regina (1)*

Source. Fols. 54v–55r. Another identical version of mm. 48–60 is preserved on fol. 56v; the reason for this replication is not clear.

Comments. Marked "Boesset" in Pechon's hand at end of work. The scoring is G2, C2, C3, F3; as such it would have been performable by both the Montmartre and *musique de la chambre* ensembles.

Notes. M. 47, "Et Jesum benedictum fructum ventris tui deux feuillets cy-apres" appears at end of measure on fol. 56v. M. 48, ¢ only on fol. 56v. M. 48, "Suitte ou faute du Salve precedent de Me Boesset" appears on fol. 56v. M. 60, "Le reste deux feuillets cy-devant" appears at end of measure. M. 61, "Reste" appears at beginning of section. Mm. 75–77, B, text is "o pia."

31. *Salve Regina (2)*

Source. Fols. 200v–201v.

32. *Salve Regina (3)*

Source. Fols. 201v–202r.

Notes. M. 28, double barline. M. 46, fermata and double barline in all parts. M. 68, fermata and double barline in all parts. M. 87, fermata and very faint double barline in all parts.

33. *Sancta Maria*

Source. Fols. 153r–v.

Note. M. 16, HC, whole note.

34. *Tu es Petrus*

Source. Fol. 188v.

Notes. M. 15, D3, notes 1–3 are b♭′. Mm. 34–38, barlines lacking.

35. *Tu es vas electionis*

Source. Fols. 189r–190r.

Notes. M. 13, D3 and HC, whole note. Mm. 58–72, coloration in source; reduced 4:1 in edition. M. 61, HC, whole note followed by two whole rests with coloration; changed to dotted breve and reduced to dotted half note. M. 65, D3, whole note followed by two whole rests with coloration; changed to breve and reduced to half note. M. 70, D3, notes 1 and 2 are f♯'.

36. Veni Sancte Spiritus

Source. Fols. 196r–v.

Notes. M. 10, D1, fermata.   M. 16, double barline.

37. Vir Domini Benedictus

Source. Fols. 210v–211r.

Notes. M. 15, D1, note 3 is f".   M. 25, HC, note 1 is whole note.   M. 28, D2, note 1 is a'.   M. 34, D2 and HC, dotted whole note.

38. Ad caenam Agni

Sources. Polyphonic setting, fol. 211v. Alternatim verset, fol. 218v; melodically concordant with *Antiphonier . . . de Montmartre*, 493.

Notes. M. 1, Meter is 3/2.   Mm. 6–7, source has "stollis" instead of "stolis."

39. Alleluja. O filii et filiae

Source. Fols. 209r–210v.

Notes. M. 10, D2, "-lu-" is on note 3.   M. 44, D2, "-lu-" is on note 3.   M. 62, D1, rhythm is half note followed by whole note.   M. 72, BD, "-lu-" is on note 2.

40. Aurea luce

Sources. Polyphonic setting, fol. 213r–v. Chant verset, fol. 219r; melodically concordant with *Antiphonier . . . de Montmartre*, 500.

Notes. Mm. 22–43, chant rhythm reduced 2:1.   M. 51, B and Org., note 2 is g.   Mm. 73–78, repeat scheme written out (*petite reprise* of mm. 67–72).

41. Ave maris stella

Sources. Polyphonic setting, fols. 212v–213r. Chant verset, fol. 219r; no concordance with *Antiphonier . . . de Montmartre*.

Comments. Source provides music for verses 1, 2, 3, 5, and "Amen" only; verses 4, 6, and 7 written out and provided with text underlay. Coloration in source for polyphony (except mm. 110–17); reduced 2:1 in edition.

Note. Mm. 22–23 (and repetitions at mm. 54–55 and 84–85), rhythm after 2:1 reduction is half note, dotted breve, breve.

42. Ave mater pia

Sources. Polyphonic setting, fols. 214r–v. Chant verset, fol. 219r; melodically concordant with *Antiphonier . . . de Montmartre*, 502.

Comments. Source provides music for first two verses only. Coloration in source for polyphony (except for mm. 49–66); both chant and polyphony reduced 2:1 in edition. Meter is **3**.

Notes. M. 14, D2, note 2 is b♭'.   M. 46, D2, note 2 is b♭'.   Mm. 53–56, rhythm displaced by addition of rest at beginning of m. 53.

43. Christe redemptor omnium, Conserva

Sources. Polyphonic setting, fol. 199r. Chant verset, fol. 219r; melodically concordant with *Antiphonier . . . de Montmartre*, 505–6.

Comment. Source provides music for first two verses only.

Notes. M. 1, meter is ¢.   M. 15, D2, note 3 is c♯".   M. 35, rhythm altered to fit underlay.

44. Christe redemptor omnium, Ex Patre

Source. Fol. 211r.

45. Claris conjubila

Sources. Polyphonic setting, fols. 213v–214r. Chant verset, fol. 219r; melodically concordant with *Antiphonier . . . de Montmartre*, 499.

Comments. Source provides music for verses 1, 2, 3, and 5 only; verse 4 written out and provided with text underlay. Rhythm of all chant verses reduced 2:1.

Note. M. 36, note 1 is breve.

46. Dionysii martyris

Sources. Polyphonic setting, fols. 197v–198r. Chant verset, fol. 219r; melodically concordant with *Antiphonier . . . de Montmartre*, 503.

Comments. Source provides music for verses 1, 2, 3, 13, and "Amen" only. Coloration in source for both chant and polyphony (except mm. 80–86); reduced 2:1 in edition. Meter is **C 3/2**.

47. Iste Confessor

Sources. Polyphonic setting, fols. 198v–199r. Chant verset, fol. 219r; melodically concordant with *Antiphonier . . . de Montmartre*, 508.

Comment. Source provides music for first two verses only.

Notes. Mm. 29–56, chant rhythm reduced 2:1; source lacks meter and barlines; an editorial suggestion is provided in the edition.   M. 90, B and Org., note 2 is c♯.

48. Jesu, nostra redemptio

Sources. Polyphonic setting, fol. 217r. Chant verset, fol. 219r; melodically concordant with *Antiphonier . . . de Montmartre*, 493–94.

Comment. Source provides music for first two verses only.

Notes. M. 58, B enters with Org. on beat 1.   M. 59, D2, note 4 is g'.

49. O gloriosae virgines

Source. Fol. 207v.

Notes. M. 14, HC, note 4 to m. 15, note 1, note tied across barline. M. 16, D2, whole note.

50. O salutaris hostia

Source. Fols. 194r–v.

51. Pange lingua . . . Corporis

Source. Fols. 211v–212r.

Notes. M. 38, single barline. M. 43, HC and B, "Tacet" in source.

52. Pange lingua . . . Certaminis

Source. Fols. 214v–215r. Though this is a through-composed polyphonic setting, a chant version for verse 2 (see appendix) also appears in the source on fol. 219r and is melodically concordant with *Antiphonier . . . de Montmartre*, 504–5.

Comment. Marked "De Sta Ursula a 4."

Notes. M. 6, source has "Virginum" instead of "Virginem." M. 48, D2, note 1 is g'.

53. Quam pulchra es

Source. Fol. 144v.

Notes. M. 4, D, half note followed by half rest. Mm. 5–7, B.c. has rests; notes taken from HT. M. 8, HT, note 3 is c'. Mm. 18–19, HT, underlay ambiguous. M. 29, D, underlay ambiguous. M. 40, D, underlay ambiguous.

53a. Quam pulchra es (alternative refrain)

Source. Fol. 193v.

Note. M. 4, D1, whole note.

54. Veni Creator Spiritus

Source. Polyphonic setting, fols. 187r–v. Chant melody lacking from source, taken from *Antiphonier . . . de Montmartre*, 494, and changed into white notation.

Appendix
Pange lingua … Certaminis, verse 2

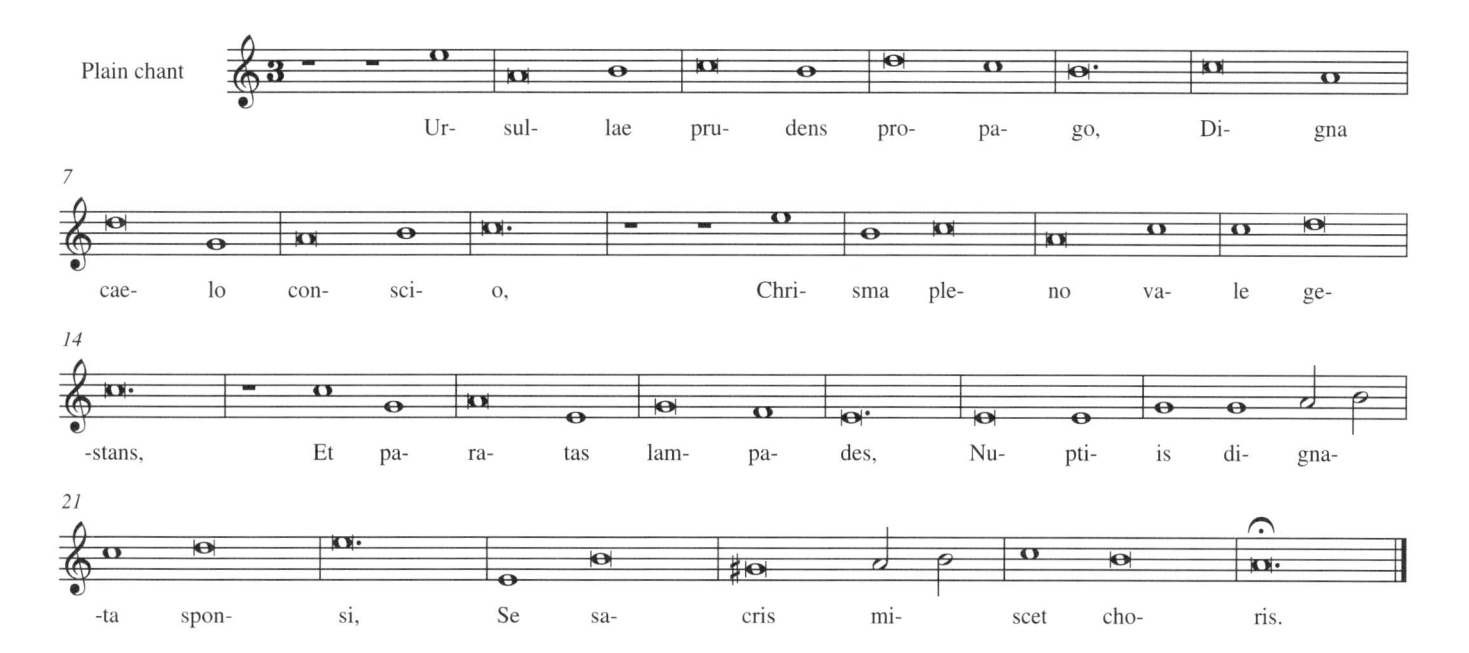

Ursullae prudens propago, Digna caelo conscio, Chrisma pleno vale gestans, Et paratas lampades, Nuptiis dignata sponsi, Se sacris miscet choris.

Recent Researches in the Music of the Baroque Era
Christoph Wolff, general editor

Vol.	Composer: Title
1	Marc-Antoine Charpentier: *Judicium Salomonis*
2	Georg Philipp Telemann: *Forty-eight Chorale Preludes*
3	Johann Caspar Kerll: *Missa Superba*
4–5	Jean-Marie Leclair: *Sonatas for Violin and Basso continuo, Opus 5*
6	*Ten Eighteenth-Century Voluntaries*
7–8	William Boyce: *Two Anthems for the Georgian Court*
9	Giulio Caccini: *Le nuove musiche*
10–11	Jean-Marie Leclair: *Sonatas for Violin and Basso continuo, Opus 9 and Opus 15*
12	Johann Ernst Eberlin: *Te Deum; Dixit Dominus; Magnificat*
13	Gregor Aichinger: *Cantiones Ecclesiasticae*
14–15	Giovanni Legrenzi: *Cantatas and Canzonets for Solo Voice*
16	Giovanni Francesco Anerio and Francesco Soriano: *Two Settings of Palestrina's "Missa Papae Marcelli"*
17	Giovanni Paolo Colonna: *Messe a nove voci concertata con stromenti*
18	Michel Corrette: *"Premier livre d'orgue" and "Nouveau livre de noëls"*
19	Maurice Greene: *Voluntaries and Suites for Organ and Harpsichord*
20	Giovanni Antonio Piani: *Sonatas for Violin Solo and Violoncello with Cembalo*
21–22	Marin Marais: *Six Suites for Viol and Thoroughbass*
23–24	Dario Castello: *Selected Ensemble Sonatas*
25	*A Neapolitan Festa a Ballo and Selected Instrumental Ensemble Pieces*
26	Antonio Vivaldi: *The Manchester Violin Sonatas*
27	Louis-Nicolas Clérambault: *Two Cantatas for Soprano and Chamber Ensemble*
28	Giulio Caccini: *Nuove musiche e nuova maniera di scriverle (1614)*
29–30	Michel Pignolet de Montéclair: *Cantatas for One and Two Voices*
31	Tomaso Albinoni: *Twelve Cantatas, Opus 4*
32–33	Antonio Vivaldi: *Cantatas for Solo Voice*
34	Johann Kuhnau: *Magnificat*
35	Johann Stadlmayr: *Selected Magnificats*
36–37	Jacopo Peri: *Euridice: An Opera in One Act, Five Scenes*
38	Francesco Severi: *Salmi passaggiati (1615)*
39	George Frideric Handel: *Six Concertos for the Harpsichord or Organ (Walsh's Transcriptions, 1738)*
40	*The Brasov Tablature (Brasov Music Manuscript 808): German Keyboard Studies 1608–1684*
41	John Coprario: *Twelve Fantasias for Two Bass Viols and Organ and Eleven Pieces for Three Lyra Viols*

42	Antonio Cesti: *Il pomo d'oro (Music for Acts III and V from Modena, Biblioteca Estense, Ms. Mus. E. 120)*
43	Tomaso Albinoni: *Pimpinone: Intermezzi comici musicali*
44–45	Antonio Lotti: *Duetti, terzetti, e madrigali a piu voci*
46	Matthias Weckmann: *Four Sacred Concertos*
47	Jean Gilles: *Requiem (Messe des morts)*
48	Marc-Antoine Charpentier: *Vocal Chamber Music*
49	*Spanish Art Song in the Seventeenth Century*
50	Jacopo Peri: *"Le varie musiche" and Other Songs*
51–52	Tomaso Albinoni: *Sonatas and Suites, Opus 8, for Two Violins, Violoncello, and Basso continuo*
53	Agostino Steffani: *Twelve Chamber Duets*
54–55	Gregor Aichinger: *The Vocal Concertos*
56	Giovanni Battista Draghi: *Harpsichord Music*
57	*Concerted Sacred Music of the Bologna School*
58	Jean-Marie Leclair: *Sonatas for Violin and Basso continuo, Opus 2*
59	Isabella Leonarda: *Selected Compositions*
60–61	Johann Schelle: *Six Chorale Cantatas*
62	Denis Gaultier: *La Rhétorique des Dieux*
63	Marc-Antoine Charpentier: *Music for Molière's Comedies*
64–65	Georg Philipp Telemann: *Don Quichotte auf der Hochzeit des Comacho: Comic Opera-Serenata in One Act*
66	Henry Butler: *Collected Works*
67–68	John Jenkins: *The Lyra Viol Consorts*
69	*Keyboard Transcriptions from the Bach Circle*
70	Melchior Franck: *Geistliche Gesäng und Melodeyen*
71	Georg Philipp Telemann: *Douze solos, à violon ou traversière*
72	Marc-Antoine Charpentier: *Nine Settings of the "Litanies de la Vierge"*
73	*The Motets of Jacob Praetorius II*
74	Giovanni Porta: *Selected Sacred Music from the Ospedale della Pietà*
75	*Fourteen Motets from the Court of Ferdinand II of Hapsburg*
76	Jean-Marie Leclair: *Sonatas for Violin and Basso continuo, Opus 1*
77	Antonio Bononcini: *Complete Sonatas for Violoncello and Basso continuo*
78	Christoph Graupner: *Concerti Grossi for Two Violins*
79	Paolo Quagliati: *Il primo libro de' madrigali a quattro voci*
80	Melchior Franck: *Dulces Mundani Exilij Deliciae*
81	*Late-Seventeenth-Century English Keyboard Music*
82	*Solo Compositions for Violin and Viola da gamba with Basso continuo*
83	Barbara Strozzi: *Cantate, ariete a una, due e tre voci, Opus 3*
84	Charles-Hubert Gervais: *Super flumina Babilonis*

85	Henry Aldrich: *Selected Anthems and Motet Recompositions*
86	Lodovico Grossi da Viadana: *Salmi a quattro cori*
87	Chiara Margarita Cozzolani: *Motets*
88	Elisabeth-Claude Jacquet de La Guerre: *Cephale et Procris*
89	Sébastien Le Camus: *Airs à deux et trois parties*
90	Thomas Ford: *Lyra Viol Duets*
91	*Dedication Service for St. Gertrude's Chapel, Hamburg, 1607*
92	Johann Klemm: *Partitura seu Tabulatura italica*
93	Giovanni Battista Somis: *Sonatas for Violin and Basso continuo, Opus 3*
94	John Weldon: *The Judgment of Paris*
95–96	Juan Bautista Comes: *Masses. Parts 1–2*
97	Sebastian Knüpfer: *Lustige Madrigalien und Canzonetten*
98	Stefano Landi: *La morte d'Orfeo*
99	Giovanni Battista Fontana: *Sonatas for One, Two, and Three Parts with Basso continuo*
100	Georg Philipp Telemann: *Twelve Trios*
101	Fortunato Chelleri: *Keyboard Music*
102	Johann David Heinichen: *La gara degli Dei*
103	Johann David Heinichen: *Diana su l'Elba*
104	Alessandro Scarlatti: *Venere, Amore e Ragione*
105	*Songs with Theorbo (ca. 1650–1663)*
106	Melchior Franck: *Paradisus Musicus*
107	Heinrich Ignaz Franz von Biber: *Missa Christi resurgentis*
108	Johann Ludwig Bach: *Motets*
109–10	Giovanni Rovetta: *Messa, e salmi concertati, op. 4 (1639). Parts 1–2*
111	Johann Joachim Quantz: *Seven Trio Sonatas*
112	Petits motets *from the Royal Convent School at Saint Cyr*
113	Isabella Leonarda: *Twelve Sonatas, Opus 16*
114	Rudolph di Lasso: *Virginalia Eucharistica (1615)*
115	Giuseppe Torelli: *Concerti musicali, Opus 6*
116–17	Nicola Francesco Haym: *Complete Sonatas. Parts 1–2*
118	Benedetto Marcello: *Il pianto e il riso delle quattro stagioni*
119	Loreto Vittori: *La Galatea*
120–23	William Lawes: *Collected Vocal Music. Parts 1–4*
124	Marco da Gagliano: *Madrigals. Part 1*
125	Johann Schop: *Erster Theil newer Paduanen*
126	Giovanni Felice Sances: *Motetti a una, due, tre, e quattro voci (1638)*
127	Thomas Elsbeth: *Sontägliche Evangelien*
128–30	Giovanni Antonio Rigatti: *Messa e salmi, parte concertati. Parts 1–3*
131	*Seventeenth-Century Lutheran Church Music with Trombones*

132	Francesco Cavalli: *La Doriclea*
133	*Music for "Macbeth"*
134	Domenico Allegri: *Music for an Academic Defense (Rome, 1617)*
135	Jean Gilles: *Diligam te, Domine*
136	Silvius Leopold Weiss: *Lute Concerti*
137	*Masses by Alessandro Scarlatti and Francesco Gasparini*
138	Giovanni Ghizzolo: *Madrigali et arie per sonare et cantare*
139	Michel Lambert: *Airs from "Airs de différents autheurs"*
140	William Babell: *Twelve Solos for a Violin or Oboe with Basso Continuo. Book 1*
141	Giovanni Francesco Anerio: *Selva armonica (Rome, 1617)*
142–43	Bellerofonte Castaldi: *Capricci (1622). Parts 1–2*
144	Georg von Bertouch: *Sonatas a 3*
145	Marco da Gagliano: *Madrigals. Part 2*
146	Giovanni Rovetta: *Masses*
147	Giacomo Antonio Perti: *Five-Voice Motets for the Assumption of the Virgin Mary*
148	Giovanni Felice Sances: *Motetti a 2, 3, 4, e cinque voci (1642)*
149	*La grand-mére amoureuse, parodie d'Atys*
150	Andreas Hammerschmidt: *Geistlicher Dialogen Ander Theil*
151	Georg von Bertouch: *Three Sacred Cantatas*
152	Giovanni Maria Ruggieri: *Two Settings of the Gloria*
153	Alessandro Scarlatti: *Concerti sacri, opera seconda*
154	Johann Sigismund Kusser: *Adonis*
155	John Blow: *Selected Verse Anthems*
156	Anton Holzner: *Viretum pierium (1621)*
157	Alessandro Scarlatti: *Venere, Adone, et Amore*
158	Marc-Antoine Charpentier: *In nativitatem Domini canticum, H. 416*
159	Francesco Scarlatti: *Six Concerti Grossi*
160	Charles Avison: *Concerto Grosso Arrangements of Geminiani's Opus 1 Violin Sonatas*
161	Johann David Heinichen: *Selected Music for Vespers*
162–63	Francesco Gasparini: *Cantatas with Violins. Parts 1–2*
164–65	Antoine Boesset: *Sacred Music. Parts 1–2*

Of Related Interest

Antoine Boesset, *Sacred Music, Part 2: Canticles, Psalms, and Masses*, edited by Peter Bennett, Recent Researches in the Music of the Baroque Era, 165

Petits Motets from the Royal Convent School at St.-Cyr, edited by Deborah Kauffman, Recent Researches in the Music of the Baroque Era, 112

Jean Gilles, *Diligam te, Domine*, edited by John Hajdu Heyer, Recent Researches in the Music of the Baroque Era, 135

Marc-Antoine Charpentier, *Nine Settings of the Litanies de la Vierge*, edited by David C. Rayl, Recent Researches in the Music of the Baroque Era, 72

For more information about these or any other volumes, see our website:
http://www.areditions.com/rr/

A-R Editions, Inc.

Middleton, Wisconsin
800 736-0070 (North American book orders)
608 836-9000 (phone)
608 831-8200 (fax)
http://www.areditions.com

ISBN 978-0-89579-676-9

DOES NOT CIRCULATE